The Optimal Staging and Phasing

of Multi-Product Capacity

SELECTED LIST OF PUBLICATIONS

A more complete list of publications appears at the end of this volume.

The Optimal Staging and Phasing of Multi-Product Capacity

Harold H. Wein
Professor of Management
Graduate School of Business Administration
Michigan State University

V. P. Sreedharan
Associate Professor of Mathematics
Michigan State University

1968
MSU STUDIES IN COMPARATIVE AND
TECHNOLOGICAL PLANNING
Institute for International Business and
Economic Development Studies
Division of Research
Graduate School of Business Administration
Michigan State University
East Lansing, Michigan

Preface

Economic planning consists of taking rational action in order to achieve future economic ends. A well formulated economic plan may be thought of as a combination of a computer program and a timetable. If all the steps in the program are carried out in the proper sequence and at the proper times, the economic plan will achieve its goals. Since it is an economic plan, it deals with scarce resources and involves, as economists put it, the optimal choice of scarce resources to attain the desired ends.

The solution to the problem of how to obtain a best combination of resources to attain some set of ends has been greatly advanced in the past two decades by the development of mathematical methods of analysis peculiarly appropriate to the problem of optimal economic choice. We refer particularly to linear programming and dynamic programming. In addition, the rapid development of electronic digital computers has greatly aided the solution of economic planning problems by its ability to rapidly execute the numerical operations involved in the application of the mathematical techniques.

In this book we are concerned with one aspect of economic planning—the optimal choice of technological projects. We think this an important planning problem—particularly if it is posed with the approximate degree of complexity in which it occurs in reality. Just what this problem is, in detail, is explained in the later chapters. The optimal investment project problem has been solved by the authors using the general dynamic programming analysis of R. Bellman. Precisely, we have constructed an algorithm which will yield an optimal solution. The mathematical analysis is given in Appendix I for those who care to go through it. So also some detailed data have been provided in Appendix II relating to steel, which is the industry to which the model was first applied. This will be of some use to those interested in steel, and in industrial applications by showing what sort of data are needed to apply the model.

Our mathematical analysis of the investment project problem developed out of a very specific planning problem involving the expansion of the Venezuelan steel industry. It was developed in order to select the best out of almost thirty technical alternatives available, many of which appeared intuitively reasonable to engineers, and some of which they would reject out of hand. One of the virtues we believe of the analysis we present is that it can operate at various levels of detail; the very fine detail in which design engineers and executives work, as well as the aggregative concepts of economists. It thus provides a bridge between the considerations of the economist, the engineer, and the executive, each of whom is involved in any real planning. In order to provide the reader with an appreciation of the practical use of the technique, Chapter IV discusses the steel problem as it appeared to the Venezuelan executives together with the results of the analysis.

The mathematical analysis is very general. What is required for its application is (a) a statement of constraints (that is to say, conditions which must be met by any solution), (b) some known technological relationship between defined inputs and outputs for each alternative, (c) some measure which is dependent upon the inputs and outputs, which it is desired to maximize or minimize over a defined time horizon, and (d) some probabilistic statement of demand of the required outputs over each period of the time horizon. It is not limited to any particular industrial sector, and it is especially useful where expansion can be accomplished in many stages distributed over time. Of course there would be no problem if there were only a very few alternatives from which to choose. In fact there are always many alternatives for most real situations. Though actual choice in the real world is usually made from only a very few alternatives, this occurs because it has not been possible to consider and evaluate all that are possible or can be generated. Heuristic methods are used most often to eliminate many alternatives involving complex interactions in order to obtain satisfactory choice. But if one is interested in optimal choices, then it is necessary to provide an algorithm that will yield an optimal choice and that will be efficient in finding it. The mathematical model we have constructed can consider a very large number of alternatives—far beyond what intuition can work with, or where choice can be made by simple numerical computation of each alternative even aided by computers. For in many problems it turns out that the number of alternatives are so large or the interactions so complex, that such brute force methods—where the computer supplies the brute force—are not feasible. Sophisticated heuristic methods such as computer simulation, can sometimes come up with satisfactory solutions to fairly complex problems. But one of the problems involved in simulated solutions of complex problems is that it is difficult to know when a satisfactory solution has been obtained and when to stop searching. An efficient analytical optimal solution on problems of the same degree of complexity possible in computer simulated systems, is obviously to be preferred to simulated solutions. In fact we think it possible with the mathematical model and algorithm we have constructed to work with greater complexity than is now possible in a simulated version of the investment project problem. One further advantage of general techniques is that they can help in the formulation of many new alternatives, particularly where it is possible to obtain new alternatives through combinations of existing ones. An example of this is given in the steel problem discussed in this book where from six basic technological designs approximately thirty separate alternatives were generated, each intuitively plausible and feasible as a matter of engineering.

Two important immediate by-products of the model may be mentioned. The problem of optimal multi-product equipment replacement under conditions of risk is easily incorporated within the general framework. This problem is simply a special case of the expansion problem in which there is only one stage of expansion. A problem closely related to the capacity expansion problem, is the reverse case in which multi-product capacity is to be withdrawn over time either because output requirements over time are falling or obsolescence, or both. Here the problem is to determine an optimal "phase-out" program. Other applications are mentioned in the later chapters.

Though much remains to be accomplished in formulating a realistic general theory of optimal technological planning for both a firm and a society, the authors believe that the methods of analysis described in this short book do provide an instrument of practical value in the optimal choice of investment projects with multi-product capacity in a single sector, under conditions of imperfect knowledge.

The authors wish to thank the Society for Industrial and Applied Mathematics for permission to reprint as Appendix I our article which appeared in the March, 1967, issue of the SIAM *Journal on Applied Mathematics.* We wish also to thank the Harvard Development Advisory Service, for the invitation to give a paper on the results of our work at their conference in Sorrento, Italy in September, 1967, a substantial part of which forms the basis of Chapters II and III. The Institute for International Business and Economic Development Studies of Michigan State University under the directorship of Robert A. Solo financed the authors in the summer of 1967, enabling them to work on this presentation, and to extend their analytical work. Our greatest obligation is to the Corporación Venezolana De Guayana, an agency of the Government of Venezuela, and to General Alfonso Ravard, President of the Corporación, and Drs. Roberto Alamo, and Pedro Maal for their assistance, both financial and intellectual, which made this research possible.

The authors also wish to acknowledge the assistance of June W. Beeson who edited the manuscript and supervised the book through production.

H. H. Wein
V. P. Sreedharan
June, 1968

Contents

List of Tables and Charts

Table

Chapter I
Technological Problems of Planning

1. The Investment Decision

One of the basic economic decisions made within every society is the choice of how much economic resources to devote to satisfying current personal consumption, and how much to devote to creating additional "means of production," that is, plants, equipment, trained manpower, and so forth. The creation of these instrumentalities of production is investment. The cost to a society of its total investment is the value of the non-investment goods, i.e., current personal consumption of goods and services—which that amount of economic resources devoted to investment goods could have yielded were it devoted to consumption goods. Investment is undertaken now in the expectation that it will result in a higher level of total output in the future. These investment decisions, as is well known, are of key importance in influencing the current level of economic activity and the pattern and level of future economic activity.

1.1 Two Distinct Investment Problems

The investment decision can be divided into two distinct though interrelated problems. There is the problem of determining the total amount of investment that should be made. We call this problem the "total investment" problem. The second problem is the selection of specific kinds of plant, equipment, or generally

1

the instrumentalities to which resources should be devoted, which we denote as the "project" problem.

Whatever answer is given to the total investment problem, nothing results until action is taken on specific ways to use these total resources. This action requires the choice of specific projects. From the point of view of one who must make a choice of specific projects, any "solution" of the total investment problem appears solely as a constraint; or a set of constraints, when "economic resources" are broken down into finer detail, such as manpower, energy, foreign exchange, and so forth. His choice of projects must not entail requirements exceeding these constraints. But as many different projects may all satisfy the constraints, there must be a way of selecting a preferred set.

2. *Normative and Empirical Theories*

When we ask what total investment should be for society as a whole, or for a specific firm or organization within that society, we presuppose some set of ends or objectives which are desired. We wish to obtain these ends or objectives in some *best* way, if that is possible. We call the set of *best* ways optimal solutions. Of course, "best" must be defined, but once it is defined, optimal solutions to both problems are possible. Our concern in this book is solely with the optimal solution of the project problem, and we are therefore dealing with normative theory.

An empirical theory explains actual events; in the context of the total investment problem, such empirical theories will explain why total investment in a society varies over time, in which direction and how much it will vary, and, most important, the economic consequences of such variation. One group of economists, macroeconomists, have always been concerned with the problems involved in determining the consequences of varying amounts of aggregate (or total) investment on the total economic activity of a society. They have also been concerned wih the factors influencing the motivation to invest. Their natural concepts are aggregative, i.e., total output, total consumption, total savings, total employment, and parallel aggregative ratios, such as income per capita, capital-output ratios, capital-labor ratios, output per man hour, and so forth. Unless they accept some social goals such as full employment, increasing per capita income, to mention only two, their work is devoid of prescriptive content—though it may be rich in explanatory content relating to the movement over time of the economic aggregates they are concerned with. Once they accept such social goals, they can prescribe economic actions and they therefore supplement economic knowledge with normative values. Economists can and do in many societies prescribe ways of inducing or restraining investment activity, as, for example, changing interest rates, wage rates, tax policy, and money supply. But their prescriptions operate on the gross levers which move the total economic activity of a society, and they must implicitly assume that their recommendations, as, for example, that total investment should be increased by some given amount, will in fact be translated into detailed, timely, and rational action. Such action involves the selection of individual investment projects and a time table for their construction, completion and operation. But the choices of specific projects and timetables require far more detailed information than economists work with, and the solutions to problems with which they are not usually concerned.

3. The Investment Problem in Different Societies

3.1 An Enterprise Economy

The total investment problem is solved in different ways in different societies. In an enterprise economy such as ours the total amount of resources devoted to investment is the resultant of independent or loosely coupled decisions made by profit making firms, nonprofit institutions, government, and individuals. The total investment decision in such a society is thus not an explicit decision made by some central authority but a resultant of thousands of decisions, most of them made without detailed knowledge of other investment decisions, and the parallel decisions of others to save, i.e., provide the resources for investment. As a consequence the total level of investment may sometimes be too low or too high—from the point of view of those who desire that an economic system serve social and economic goals, such as, for example, full employment. In virtually all well developed enterprise economies, government attempts to adjust the total level of investment and consumption by manipulating what we have called the gross levers—attempting to steer a path which avoids substantial unemployment, and substantial inflation, and at the same time enables the economy to grow and achieve other social goals. No single group in such an enterprise society, no matter how large, plans the total pattern and level of investment. Rather all investment making groups including government react to the existing state of total economic activity and their estimates of its future states. And the future state of economic activity including the total level of investment (and consumption) is a function of their reactions.

The economy as a whole in an enterprise society is a sort of black box to each of the economic decision-making entities within it, part of whose structure is known and part unknown. There is no normative theory of total planning for an enterprise economy, for the simple reason that there is no total plan accepted by all. There are, however, plans which each economic decision-making entity in such an economy attempts to follow—from government and huge corporations down to the very smallest decision-making groups. Their plans must be made in the face of considerable uncertainty about the future—and a great deal of the uncertainty is inherent in the decentralized, quasi-autonomous nature of the economic decision-making bodies. Their investment planning is nevertheless intended to be rational given their ends, information, and constraints. They must solve the two investment problems—that is to say, the total investment problem and the project problem. Whether they accept a satisfactory solution or search for an optimal one is largely a function of their perception of the problem and the cost and time constraints within which they must decide.

3.2 A Centrally Planned Economy

A society that is completely directed in its economic aspects by some central authority faces the same two problems. Its central planning authority must, however, make explicit decisions on how much total output it wishes to obtain over time (its economic growth rate), and how much of this output each period it wishes to (or must) devote to investment goods and services and to consumption goods and services. As the firm in an enterprise economy, once it chooses a level of total investment, must get down to the hard detail of specific projects—to the logistics as it were of the investment decision, so also the central planners must assure themselves that the logistics of the thousands of individual investment projects which make up their "plan" are internally consistent, and actually possible. "Internally consistent" means simply that the completion of one project does not make it impossible to complete some other project within the time schedule of each project. "Actually possible" means that the constraints chosen are realistic and consistent as a set. For example, the output planned over some time period, cannot require manpower inputs that exceed what will be available over this time period. And if there is more than one constraint they must be consistent.

In principle, the planners of a centralized society and the planners of an individual firm in an enterprise society are engaged in a very similar formal problem. The criteria determining what is an optimal choice will differ, the constraints may differ, and the objectives will differ. But both are engaged in choosing an optimal set of alternatives under conditions of imperfect knowledge about the future (risk) given objectives for which the relationship between inputs and outputs (the technological structure of each alternative or project) are known. Both operate within a system of economic accounting in which inputs can be given a cost, outputs a value, and the units of both are commensurable. Both are attempting to plan the future by engaging in acts and decisions in the present. One is attempting to plan the level of economic activity and its detailed character for an entire society, the other for only an individual firm or small component of society.

The central planners of an economy view the entire relevant future path of the economy as subject to their control in the relevant aspects. There are for them no blind economic forces outside their control—though obviously there are natural forces outside their control. The central planners of a firm cannot so view the economy in which they operate. The future state of the economy—both its gross level of activity and its detailed character are outside their control. It is more like a force of nature—something which must be reckoned with and forecast and in this manner incorporated in their planning.

4. *Project and Total Investment*

The following simple diagram illustrates the relationship between total investment and individual projects.

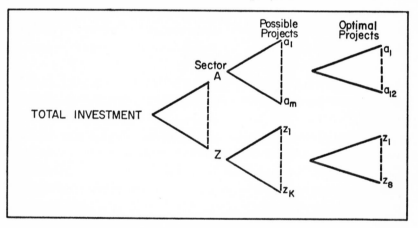

The diagram refers to some time period, say n years. Time must be taken into account since many projects require years to complete and they are set up to satisfy anticipated demands or outputs which run over different time periods. In general, wherever there are advantages in building large scale units (as plant) rather than smaller ones, and demand is expected to increase (or decrease) over time, there always is a problem of how to match capacity which almost always comes in discrete quantity with a varying demand over time. Thus total investment planning always involves problems of timing and it is for this reason that we have characterized it as a combination of a computer program and a time table. Selecting an optimal project within some particular sector—or project planning also involves the time table aspect. For, given the demand which varies over time and the fact that individual projects can be built in stages, one must select the points in times when the project should be built (either as a whole or piecemeal) in order to minimize or maximize whatever the objectives are over the planning period.

It should be noted that for the economy as a whole, the basic economic equality i.e., total output equals total investment plus total consumption, always holds. The commensurability of the units of each term are of course assumed, and the equality maintains balance in the system of accounting. From the aggregative viewpoint from which macro-economists view an economic system, given an existing output—and capacity to produce goods and services, once a value is given to total investment say I_j, we can consider that the total investment problem is solved since the basic decision has been made which divides the total available output between consumption and investment. But the question as to how this total value I_j is arrived at is far from solved. For as the diagram shows, the total must still be divided into specific projects, and in general this relationship is one-many, i.e., a total can be composed of many different sets of numbers, all different, but all summing to the same value. Very little information is given on how to go about selecting from the entire available population of possible proposed projects (a_l to z_k in the diagram) some smaller, subset of optimal projects, which will add up to or be less than, I_j. If I_j is in fact determined, it acts as a constraint on the subset— that is to say, it sets an upper bound on the total value of investment in the whole subset. If it is possible to divide I_j into sectors from A to Z and allocate some of the resources to each sector, then sharper constraints are placed on the projects, but the solution to the problem of how to choose the optimal subset of projects in sectors A through Z is not further advanced. If it happens, as it sometimes does, that all available projects in sector A, (projects

a_1 to a_m in the above diagram) will require less capital than allocated to sector A_{a1} then there is no problem of project choice in sector A, all the projects a_1 to a_m will be funded—even if they are not very good projects. Even worse, under some bureaucratic organizations, projects will be created of marginal value to use up the available resources allocated to sector A.

Such results—which are very common in all large organizations—come about due to the fact that aggregation is a convenient device for some expository and bargaining purposes. It thus becomes easy to assume that there are real economic relationships between total investment and sector investment (i.e., "steel"—or worse still "metals," "energy," and so forth). In fact these are mere classificatory devices, which do not necessarily reflect technological relationships between projects (one serves as a source of inputs to another). Input-output tables show such interrelationships in economic terms, i.e., value, for gross classifications of industries for a particular period of time. For optimal planning of projects and their interrelationships, such information is far too coarse.

It should be noted that no arrows are shown on the diagram. Many planners depending upon their position in the organization (either firm or economy) work as if the direction of the arrows must necessarily proceed from left to right, i.e., from total investment to sectors to projects, or from the general to the particular. In fact, if these were arrows, they must show a two-way flow— since total investment will be a function of the intrinsic worth (or expected value of the outcomes of each project) balanced against the total resources and the claims of consumption.

The selection of nonoptimal projects within a single sector, means costs are higher and output lower than they could be. There cannot therefore be an optimal solution of the total investment problem without an optimal solution of the project problem. On the other hand, the selection of an optimal project within a single sector, is not the same problem as the selection of an optimal set of investment projects for the economy as a whole. The interrelationships between projects are indeed extremely complex, and single sector optimal solutions are highly likely to be suboptimal for an entire economy. Nevertheless, it is important to solve even the partial problem, particularly as the general problem to our knowledge has not been solved—and may not be possible to solve. Further most decision makers within an enterprise or mixed economy and even those in a centrally planned economy usually work on single sector or partial solutions.

5. *Error and Planning*

Even the poet knows that the "plans of mice and men go awry," but it is nevertheless surprising to see how many plans are made on the assumption that knowledge of the present and the future is perfect. No economy, whatever its structure, has complete control over all the elements which will influence its plans, nor do firms have such control. Knowing that forces exist which tend to frustrate, or deteriorate plans, or which change the factual presuppositions of the plans, how can these forces be taken account of in the structure of the plans themselves?

It is not enough to say that the planning was successful but the results expected were not achieved because conditions changed or, as they say in the medical world, the operation was successful but the patient died from complicating factors. Substantial errors in economic planning and in real investment planning have serious harmful consequences which show up in similar ways in both centrally directed and enterprise economies, and the smaller scale planning of firms. The failure to meet the plan targets of a centrally directed economy is an obvious failure of planning, though the reasons for failure may be far from obvious. Substantial unemployment, inflation, bottlenecks resulting in shortages in particular goods and services or in particular geographical regions, excess capacity long sustained in some sectors of the economy, production of goods and services that must be sold below cost, failure of firms, and the creation of social burdens and costs such as slums, water and air pollution, and traffic congestion are the marks of planning errors in both economies.

5.1   *Sources of Error*

(a) *Forces of Nature.* Sometimes plans either for an economy or a sector are not achieved due to forces of nature intervening in unpredictable ways, such as floods, drouth, insects, excessive heat or cold, and so forth. Agricultural plans are upset, power supply based upon hydro-electric sources is far less than expected —all traced back to these natural forces. But all these phenomena of nature are well known, they are subject to probability distributions that are usually known. They should be taken into account in an optimal plan not by the empty phrase "calculated risk" but by actual risk calculations and the provision of alternatives after calculation of the probable costs and benefits of alternative means of meeting these natural hazards. Thus in hydro-electric planning engineers do not simply plan on the average head of the river, but create artificial lakes or reservoirs to even the flow in times of excess and deficient supply.

(b) *Failures of Human Forces.* Closely related to the unpredictable natural forces and much more important as a reason for the failure of what appear to be satisfactory or even optimal plans are the failures of execution. These are forces of nature in the guise of refractory human conduct. A steel plant might be chosen on the expectation that it will achieve normal efficiency in two years. It does not achieve normal efficiency for seven years. Output is much below what had been expected and costs much higher.

(c) *Errors in Forecasting the Future.* This is a very common source of failure in planning. In the U. S. economy where a firm may be planning an expansion in some single sector of its activities, or in a particular geographical region, demand forecasts are virtually always the first data step. But demand forecasts are notoriously unreliable particularly where one must deal with a fairly long planning horizon—say, ten to twenty years in the future. Other factors must also be forecast, such as relative costs of inputs and so forth. What forecasts should one rely upon? Depending upon the error, the planned and created capacity might be too low or too high with varying degrees of excess costs in either case.

(d) *Errors Due to Complexity.* These errors result from the failure to comprehend the consequences of the numerous inter-relationships involved and the consequences of different degrees of plan achievement in each of the components of a plan involving numerous separate projects. Central planning is greatly affected by such errors, which result in unanticipated and undesirable consequences forcing modification, drastic or moderate as the case may be. Many of these errors due to complexity arise from inability to incorporate into planning the sorts of errors mentioned in (a) through (c) above. That is to say the total plan may have been constructed with too little attention given to the cumulative effects of errors in component plans on the operation of the total plan. Thus if one planned on a certain amount of agricultural output on the basis of average rainfall, insect conditions, and temperature, and unfortunately made no provision for harmful departures from the average—such as stocks of food, etc., many other components of a total plan would be seriously injured. Food may have to be purchased from abroad, depleting foreign exchange, preventing purchase of foreign equipment needed for some other sector, etc.

The more complex a plan, the more it is subject to the forces of nature and of man which tend to deteriorate an interconnected structure. Even if all total plans were optimally constructed in the choice of components, i.e., each project were selected optimally with explicit building into the optimal choice algorithm the various stochastic factors involved, there would still be a problem of the reliablity of the total system. Some systems will crumble more rapidly and more extensively than others under the same set of deteriorating stresses. Electrical engineers, and biologists, for example, have long been aware of the importance of such phenomena in the systems they study. Economists have been aware of negative and positive feedback in economic systems. In Western economies much attention is given to forecasting future economic conditions and to constructing institutions and policies to aid government in moderating the frequency and amplitude of economic fluctuations subject to feedback phenomena. But the formal analysis of the reliability of optimal economic planning models involving choice of different technical alternatives in a real time setting, is to our knowledge extremely scarce. Our own work on this has barely begun and we can give no help in this problem. But it is important to highlight it, since it is, we believe, a basic problem of all serious planning.

6.   *Taking Account of Error in Project Planning*

Where the problem is to choose some particular project from a set of alternatives conceived to achieve some stipulated set of end products or services, the serious problems of error lie in the predictions or factual parameters of the problem. What are the estimated demands for each of the products of the multiproduct facility—what is their variance, are they stable probability distributions over time, are the technical relationships accurate and stable, will the prices of inputs vary over the future, and similar questions must be answered. The answers are all subject to varying degrees of error and so our choice of an optimal project must be based upon stochastic conditions if it is to be of relevance to the real problem. The ramifications of these difficulties in the problem of optimal project choice is explained in the succeeding chapters. Appendix I gives the mathematical analysis which shows in detail how one can treat probabilistic questions in an optimal algorithm.

Chapter II
The Project Problem

1. *The Problem of Expanding Industrial Capacity*

The problem of expanding industrial capacity in some specific sector can be treated as the same formal problem for developed and underdeveloped countries, though the constraints and the objectives can, of course, be quite different. Also, whether a firm or a government agency is the decision-making center is not relevant to the abstract problem or its solution. In the mathematical analysis of this problem, we have incorporated certain features that are of special importance to underdeveloped economies, and have set some constraints that might not be appropriate to a developed economy or a private firm.[1]

1.1 *Sector and Economy-Wide Expansion*

Underdeveloped economies face two distinct though interrelated problems. The first is the capital budget problem. That is, which subset of a list of suggested expansion programs should be selected given a (finite) capital budget. For underdeveloped economies, shortage of capital is almost always an important constraint, though not the only one, since trained manpower and

---

1. V. P. Sreedharan, H. H. Wein, "A Stochastic, Multi-Stage, Multi-Product, Investment Model," *Society of Industrial and Applied Mathematics (Siam) Journal of Applied Mathematics*, XV, 2, March, 1967. This article is reprinted here as Appendix I.

foreign exchange constraints are usually present as well. The second problem is how to select in some particular sector that specific program, i.e., that particular industrial facility and its phasing over time, which is in some clearly defined sense, optimal. It is to the solution of this problem that our analysis is directed.

The total investment problem or the capacity expansion problem of an entire economy over some defined time period cannot be said to be *optimally* solved unless one has solved also the investment problem of each sector of the economy in its interactions. That is to say, the simultaneous solution of the investment problem of each and all (possibly dependent) sectors is required. The textbook solutions of the capital budget problem assume among other things that projects are independent, and also that the profitability or cost of each project is in fact known over the time horizon. This latter problem is indeed the problem we grapple with under realistic conditions.

1.2 *The Realistic Sector Expansion Problem*

These realistic conditions include:

(a) Facilities (plant and equipment) which can produce more than one product.

(b) Facilities which are capable of being built piecemeal, over time.

(c) Choice of optional location for a particular plant or industrial facility (single plant location).

(d) Estimates of demand for each of the products over the time horizon, which are at best known only as some probability distribution.

(e) Many alternative possibilities of plant and equipment in a particular sector are available; these alternatives can number many hundreds or thousands.

(f) The length of the planning period to choose is itself not known.

(g) Different degrees of difficulty of operations are associated with each alternative.

(h) The whole process of expansion is viewed as taking place in time so that for each alternative one must solve precisely when the expansion or expansions of capacity must take place in order to minimize costs (or maximize profits) of each expansion alternative presented.

If one can choose an optional expansion program under all these conditions, then the solution of the single sector expansion problem has been obtained under fairly realistic conditions. Conditions (b), (c), (g) and (h) are all time-determined (a function of time) and so it is apparent that we deal with a complex variety of dynamic programming in the capacity expansion problem of a single sector. For underdeveloped economies, we wish to solve a related problem, i.e, the problem of optimal mix of imports (say, that of flat steel products) and local production.

In the actual analysis of the Venezuelan flat steel products expansion, the problem of location was not treated since the location was given. However, the mathematical analysis is general enough to include the solution of single plant location. The problem of learning curves associated with each alternative was not treated due to lack of data. This problem also can, without too much difficulty, be incorporated into the analysis.

The heart of the mathematical difficulty lies in condition (h) above. That is, the solution of the capacity expansion problem consists in specifying the precise times within the planning period when for each alternative we achieve a minimum (in the case of costs) or a maximum (in the case of profits). Comparing all the alternatives yields the best, i.e., a minimum minimorum, or maximum maximorum. Our effort is, therefore, focused on the problem of determining the optimal time phasing for some one alternative which is completely specified *except* for this phasing.

It should be noted that the optimal solution is optimal only with respect to the list of alternatives presented for analysis, and the other information available. Further, optimal sector solutions may be and probably are suboptimal in terms of an economy-wide expansion problem. Since no one to our knowledge has given an analytic solution to the economy-wide expansion problem, we think it useful to solve the simpler one-sector problem—that is, the dynamic, multistage, multiproduct, one-sector problem under conditions of probabalistic demand (or requirements). We believe it useful for the following reasons: The solution of the single-sector problem in adequate realistic detail will help in the formulation and perhaps in the solution of the "n" sector problem[2]; all actual decisions on single sector expansion are now made without an analytically optimal solution of either the single-sector or "n" sector problem; the difference between single-sector solutions can be very substantial. And so it is a matter of considerable practical importance to obtain the best of these suboptimal solutions, where, as in the expansion of steel capacity or other major industrial expansions, expenditures of tens or hundreds of millions of dollars are involved; if optimal single-sector solutions were obtained for all sectors in which expansion was considered, considerable help would be given to overall expansion planning even though no formal analytic optimal program for the entire economy can be demonstrated.

1.3 *Comparison of the Realistic Single-Sector Analysis and Conventional Economic-Engineering Evaluation*

Engineering-economy evaluations of alternatives involved in expansion plans of industrial projects are almost uniformly characterized by the following:

(a) A relatively small list of alternatives are examined, usually less than ten, and most often five or less.

(b) Demand for the products over time is invariably given as single or point estimates for each year over the planning period. That is to say the demand or requirements are treated as if they were certain—or error free. Where errors are acknowledged, no attempt is made to systematically include them in the analysis.

(c) Most technical processes are compared as single-stage expansions. Where the possibility of staging is recognized,

---

2. We have recently solved the problem of optimal expansion of two related sectors, i.e., where one sector provides the input to another, a step perhaps in the solution of the "n" interrelated sectors problem.

standard or conventional staging is assumed as fully integrated, semi-integrated or nonintegrated.

(d) The key problem of determining the precise time phasing over the planning horizon when the processes or its stages should be introduced in order to yield a minimum cost (or maximum profit) is ignored. Arbitrary phasing is used such as comparing all the processes at an identical starting time, or comparing them at times determined by lead times (i.e., times of construction and procurement).

(e) A very restricted list of feasible parameter values is used.

(f) The assumption is made that all operating costs are "standard" costs, i.e., those costs which would prevail once normally efficient operations have been achieved. The differences in amount of time (or amount of output) necessary to achieve these standard costs which may vary with the type of process are ignored.

(g) Optimal mixes of different sizes of equipment are based upon informed judgment rather than upon systematic examination and analysis. In the rare case in which this is done by systematic analysis, it is usually done by linear programming methods which assume away the time phasing problem (i.e., the fact that demand is a function of time and hence changes each year or period).

(h) The location problem is treated as if it were independent of the alternative processes; and where costs of transportation to markets are important, the fact that regional demand over time will change is ignored in the actual computations.

(i) In the case of underdeveloped economies, the optimal mix between imports and local production is not solved or even treated.

(j) The time horizon is fixed (i.e., 10 years or 15 years or 20 years). No attempt is made to determine the effect on the choice of alternatives of different lengths of the time horizon.

1.4   *Errors of Phasing and Staging*

On the basis of our formulation and analysis of the single sector expansion problem, such engineering-economic evaluations will not, except by accident, achieve the optimal solution of even the restricted number of alternatives examined by such studies. For it is clear that where output and costs are a function of time, there is no optimal *process*. There is an optimal program which can only be obtained through correct choice of the (technological) *process*, the *stages* of the process, and the *time phasing*. Correct choice, of course, means that choice which minimizes or maximizes whatever it is we are minimizing or maximizing under the constraints. Since each technical process may, in general, have different numbers of possible stages and such stagings may have different phasing for which it is optimal, these processes cannot be validly compared, except at their optimal staging and phasing, within the planning period. It follows then that arbitrary staging (comparing all processes as if they had to be installed as single-stage processes) and arbitrary phasing (comparing all processes from the same date of operation) will not provide valid comparisons of the processes.[3] For example, the differences over the planning period in total discounted costs arising from arbitrary phasing of the alternative processes will, of course, be different from those differences under optimal phasing. Choice can thus be distorted. Arbitrary phasing will be biased towards favoring those processes whose optimal phasing happens to be at or close to the arbitrary phasing time compared to those processes whose optimal phasing is more distant from the uniform or arbitrary phasing time. Even in single-stage processes such bias may result in choosing a process (defined in a technological sense) different from the optimal one. Even if the process chosen is technologically identical with that chosen under optimal phasing, waste occurs (i.e., excessive costs or lower profits). Where multiple stages of the same technological process are compared, arbitrary phasing will yield the same sorts

---

3. The dates of the planning period or time horizon are, of course, the same for all processes (e.g., 1970-1990); but the dates when the processes should be operational within that period need not be the same.

of errors as in single-stage arbitrary phasing and could, moreover, lead to the choice of a nonoptimal number of stages. These sorts of errors will not be revealed in income statements or through conventional cost accounting. They are opportunity errors arising from a faulty planning analysis and cannot be ascertained unless the alternative opportunities were calculated from the beginning in the planning analysis.

It is worth pointing out that in underdeveloped countries there often is considerable pressure to start certain industrial expansions as soon as possible, particularly in steel which has much glamour, perhaps as a result of the Russian emphasis on heavy industry. A starting date may be, therefore, politically determined. The value of our analytical model in this case consists of showing the shadow price or the additional expense (or loss of profit) which this politically determined date incurs. Moreover, in the case of multistage expansion it can compute what the optimal time phasings should be for all the other stages of each alternative examined, given the constraint that all the first stages must be built at the politically determined date.

1.5 Errors of Limited Alternatives

In addition to the errors which result from arbitrary phasing, another source of error resulting from conventional analysis is the restriction of the analysis to a very few technical alternatives and to a very small range of feasible parameter values. No mathematical analysis can do more than evaluate what is presented to it. If the list of expansion alternatives is small, the mathematical analysis can choose the best of the small list. However, it can also choose the best of a very large list since the mathematical analysis can be combined with computer operations. The ability to see a reasonably full range of the available economic and technical options requires a creative combination of engineering and applied economics.

One of the problems of planning both in underdeveloped and developed economies is that, unfortunately, very few options are offered for analysis. And, paradoxically, this is often due to the fact that there are so many that they cannot be evaluated by conventional engineering-economic methods. For example, in a rather simple integrated flat product steel works analyzed by three British engineers, 1,368 compatible single-stage processes are shown.[4] It is evident that conventional analysis of all of these processes is not possible even without bringing in such realistic complications as uncertain demand, many different parameter values (interest rate, salvage rate, etc.), multistage possibilities, and so forth. The heuristic method of "judgment" must be used. Even if we were to computerize all the necessary calculations and solve each staging and phasing problem in this example by brute force methods, then, assuming an average of three stages, a twenty-year planning horizon, the 96 feasible sets of parameter values we found feasible in the Venezuelan problem, and assuming certain demand estimates, over 50,000 hours or about eight to ten years of CDC 3600 (a pretty large scale computer) operation would be necessary to choose the optimal program. Clearly, we need some powerful algorithm which will give us the solution without computing out each possibility. The mathematical model (and its associated computer program) is given in a simplified model in Chapter III. On the basis of our experience with the Venezuelan flat steel products problem, the analogous British example would require in the order of 1000 hours or a saving of about 98 percent of the total computer time. One thousand hours is still a great deal of computer time. If the problem were actually given for solution, preliminary analysis would probably reveal that many stages could be discarded so that further savings of computer time could be achieved.

1.6 *Errors Due to Assumption of Standard Costs*

The problem of "learning curves" or the time it will take before a new plant will achieve standard operating efficiency has not generally been taken into account as a factor in selecting a sector

---

4. Brisby, Worthington and Anderson, "Economics of Process Selection in the Iron and Steel Industry," *Journal of the Iron and Steel Institute (U.K.)*, Sept., 1963, p. 727.

expansion program. In underdeveloped countries where trained engineering, managerial, and manual workers are often in very short supply, it can be a factor of considerable consequence. That is so because different technical processes often have different degrees of difficulty associated with them. As a consequence, different industrial facilities facing the same demand and having the capacity to meet this demand will have different levels of output and costs other than the costs "standard" for such facility at that output. Steel plants are particularly subject to this varying difficulty of operation. Open-hearth furnaces, for example, are much more difficult to operate than electric furnaces or basic oxygen furnaces. And if one starts out with a work force (managerial, technical, and manual) which has little experience, serious errors can result from comparing all processes as if this difference did not exist. In effect the costs of the inputs (labor, materials, etc.) and the amount of the output vary over time not only because output varies over time, but because the physical coefficients will not attain their standard or designed values until the technology is mastered. Such information is hard to come by, but experienced operating personnel and consulting engineers can often give estimates of the time it would usually take. If this information is available, it can be built into the mathematical model we have constructed. On the basis of a detailed study of the operations of the Orinoco Steel Plant which we undertook, it was clear that this factor of learning was different in different parts of the operation and was an important factor explaining the inability of the plant to achieve scheduled output.[5] The presumption of many economists that underdeveloped economies should concentrate on minimizing capital by substituting labor ignores this consideration— since plants with the higher capital (more capital intensive) are usually more automated and less difficult to master.

1.7 *The Optimal Size of Component Equipment*

A major industrial facility is a complex and unique structure.

---

5. H. H. Wein, P. Maal, V. P. Sreedharan, "Operation of the Orinoco Steel Plant," (Caracas: Corporación Venezolana De Guayana, Oct. 1, 1964), p. 186.

Fortunately, like most unique things it usually consists of different combinations of modular components. For many of these components, knowledge is very great and experienced engineers can without much difficulty choose the correct ones to use. For other significant components, the choice of types and sizes (or capacities) of these components which are optimal is not intuitively clear.

An example may be taken from the steel industry. Suppose alternative plans for the raw steel making stage had been proposed with various total capacities and made by four basic furnace types as follows: open hearth, LD, Kaldo, and electric furnace. In the various designs of these plants based upon each furnace type, the engineers had used furnace sizes customarily used with the alternative capacities they were testing. Using our model, suppose we had been able to determine that the optimal plant consisted of 1,000,000 tons of LD to be installed at t_1; 1,000,000 at t_2; and 600,000 at t_3. Now on the information given this plant is optimal, but the question could and should be raised as to whether the furnace sizes chosen were in fact the optimal furnace sizes—since there could be significant differences in cost between furnaces of the same type but of different size, as well as between furnaces of different types given a set of input costs. If this is the case, then in fact the optimal solution need not be optimal unless one chose the optimal furnace sizes given the information on demand, costs of inputs, capital cost, and so forth. A steel plant based upon a 100-ton LD furnace (which would yield about 660,000 tons per year) would be a somewhat different steel plant than one based upon a 150-ton furnace. A larger furnace would require larger ladles (or more small ladles), heavier cranes, more massive crane runways, heavier columns, stronger foundations, and so forth. Moreover, there is also the possibility of mixing sizes (i.e., one 100-ton furnace, one 150-ton furnace, etc.) and of mixing types (i.e., LD and electric), for example. Such is the fecundity of permutations and combinations, that given four basic types and five feasible sizes, say, in each type, and the possibility of mixing types one can easily run into several thousand unique possibilities, for each of which the steel plant design could be different.

The difficulty is not in obtaining the enumeration of all the combinations of sizes, types and mixtures—one could easily construct a simple computer routine to enumerate all of them; the difficulty lies in the expense of designing the remainder of the plant and equipment around these different combinations. Steel plant design has not yet been reduced to computer algorithms—though probably this also will be done. If one wished to use our model on this problem one would have to define each combination of furnace type and size together with all the attendant costs (i.e., not only of the furnaces themselves, but of the balance of plant and equipment which goes with them). This in effect requires plant designs for each combination of furnaces. Though we would have lots of computations—perhaps of the order of several hundred hours of computation—the algorithm would then come up with the optimal design including the furnace size and type as well as the phasing of these. But that would entail an enormous waste of a scarce talent—design engineering, if it could be done at all within the necessary time constraints.

A more effective way to do it would be to take advantage of the relatively small number of designs based upon the original analysis where the "judgmental" appropriate types and sizes of furnaces were used. One assumes that all other parts of the design are as initially given, and all that changes are the costs pertaining solely to the furnaces themselves. This is obviously not true, but certainly it is a first approximation, and avoids the necessity of thousands of steel plant designs. There is still a great deal of information required, but it is information which is known; if it were not, the problem of optimal furnace size would not be soluble to begin with. Re-evaluating the analysis will now give another answer on the basis of the first approximation costs of the remainder of the plant. Given the difference between the first answer and the second answer, we know the difference in the discounted costs over the planning period due to the inclusion of the various furnace sizes and types. The additional costs of the new facility designed around these components can easily be estimated to see whether a significant improvement has been made. The optimal plant can then be designed in detail and the phasing of the second approximation checked by re-evaluation—now, of only one alternative—which is a matter of less than a minute of computer time.

It would be both more elegant and efficient if one could use general formulae expressing the variation of costs with size of furnace type and output, and avoid having to examine each size furnace and combinations of different sizes and types. We have not, as yet, been able to incorporate such general formulae into our model. Nevertheless, though with the present model we require a great deal of computer time to solve for the optimal process including the optimal size of important components, we do get a great deal for this computation (i.e., the optimal phasing, staging, important component size, and mix of local production and imports) for a greatly expanded list of alternatives under conditions of probabalistic demand for multiproduct industrial facilities. Moreover, where necessary one can incorporate the problems of "learning" phenomena and single plant location.

1.8 *Why the Model Is Versatile*

The versatility of the model for the various subproblems of a realistic expansion problem arises from the abstract definitions of a "process" and "process stage." A process is nothing more (or less) than a unique combination of plant and equipment, designed to some capacity in each of its products (one or more). A process stage, or stage of a process, is some operational part of the process which can produce one or more products (including the complete product range) but not the maximum capacity in each product. Clearly, all processes can be built in one stage, and many (virtually all) major industrial facilities can be built in more than one stage. For each process or stage, of course, one must have the requisite information on capacity capital outlay and operating costs.[6]

The level of detail of the answers obviously depends upon the level of detail of the inputs. So far as the mathematics is concerned, a process and process stage are vectors—which translate what is relevant for choice of the engineering design into a set of numbers. Evaluating whole plant designs is a different and simpler problem than is *optimally* designing or selecting all the components of the plant as well. When it is important to select optimally certain major components—then we must define as a separate process different component alternatives together with all the differences the variation of that component will make in the total design. As we have indicated, the number of component possibilities is very great and several evaluations will result in great savings in actual engineering designs. Where transportation costs of both inputs and outputs are important, an optimal plant design involving different choices of the technologies though the same product outputs, must be based as well on the solution of the optimal location. The best single plant location—the cost effects of each location—is incorporated into the "process," that is to say, an identical facility at two different locations becomes two separate processes and this is also true for the process stages.

2. The Economic Strategy of Steel Expansion— The Venezuelan Case

2.1 Demand for Flat Steel Products

The market for steel in Venezuela should grow rapidly. The Gross National Product was estimated by Venezuelan authorities to expand at an average rate of about 8 percent per year in the foreseeable future. Steel-using sectors of the economy will expand at least at that rate. There will be some substitution of steel end products for non-steel end products, as well as import substitution, so that overall steel requirements will probably grow at a rate higher than the total national output. Further, there is

---

6. In practical work it is necessary to take into account that the sum of the investment costs of the stages well exceed the investment outlay of the facility built completely in one stage (price constant) due to the large start-up costs of construction, and some necessary alterations of design arising from staging as, for example, possibly greater storage capacity, etc.

the possibility that Latin American economic growth may provide substantial steel export markets for Venezuela, if not hampered by nationalistic considerations.

Venezuela currently does not produce plates, sheets, strip, tin plate, or galvanized sheets. The imports of these products in 1963 amounted to roughly 100 million Bolivars, and 137,000 tons. Given the national plans for economic development and judging by past trends, there was little doubt among the Venezuelans and their consultants that the demand for flat products would increase substantially in future years at a higher rate than the average of all primary steel products. It is natural, therefore, that flat products capacity has a high priority compared with other possible additions to Venezuelan steel capacity.

2.2 *Demand Projections and the Problem of Error*

The single most critical economic judgment which must be made in expanding steel capacity is the estimate of demand for the various types of finished steel products over the planning period. Once these estimates are accepted, limits are placed upon the size of the entire iron and steel complex, and upon the range of processes and equipment which are feasible.

The one fairly certain aspect of future Venezuelan steel demand is that over the foreseeable future, it will continue to grow. No demand estimate is error free, even those pertaining to well-developed economies and based upon refined techniques, such as econometric analysis, input-output analysis, and so forth. The usefulness of econometric models for long-term forecasting (say, five years and more) depends upon the stability of the structural parameters over time, the precision of the model and upon the accuracy of the forecasts of the exogenous variables, i.e., those variables taken as independent. In the input-output method, one must know whether the technological coefficients will remain relatively stable over time, and the size and composition of final demand in the future. In short, there is no way to predict the future value of a variable without predicting the variable directly or predicting the future value of some other variables upon which the variable of interest depends.

One might obtain better predictions of steel requirements of Venezuela than by direct prediction if one had an input-output analysis of the entire Venezuelan economy in detail, not only as it now exists but as it will be in the future. Of course, this is not possible for an economic system which is not almost completely planned, or one which like Venezuela will undergo rapid transformation in the future. Moreover, refined econometric techniques which might give better estimates of steel demand for future years usually require long-time series; input-output analysis is not useful for long-term prediction unless very strong (and doubtful) assumptions are made, and unless detailed industrial sector information is available.[7] Needless to say, the data available for such sophisticated analysis of Venezuelan steel requirements from 1965 through 1980 or 1985, are not now available. A major economic and statistical effort, taking several years, would be required to obtain such information. Moreover, once obtained it would not obviate the necessity of making some forecast of the exogenous variables.

Our view is that given the present state of economic data in Venezuela, direct estimates of steel requirements based upon past data and future economic plans, checked against performance of other countries, is probably the best that can be done. To this extent, we follow the simple method of projecting annual rates of growth. We differ from most such treatments in our explicit recognition that these estimates are subject to error and we take

---

7. See, for example, the recently completed input-output study of the U.S. Department of Commerce in the November, 1964, issue of the *Survey of Current Business*, which identifies 86 separate industrial sectors. As this study is based on 1958 Census data, the information is already nine years old. Doubtlessly well-developed economies change their structure of production and final demand only slowly, so that the 1958 input-output structure might be a reasonably accurate picture of 1964 in the U.S.A. But would it be for 1974? Clearly, for rapidly changing economies such as Venezuela, it would not be.

four estimates of such error into explicit account in our projections of steel demand.[8] The way we do this is explained below.

The problem of error in demand forecasts raises a fundamental policy issue, with respect to steel expansion. This issue may be put in the form of the following question. Is it in the best interest of Venezuela to make an error in steel expansion which results in building x percent too much capacity; or is it preferable to make an error which results in building x percent too little capacity? Clearly, there is no prior wisdom which can state that the costs of equal though opposite errors (x percent too much capacity versus x percent too little capacity) are equal. Obviously, if the errors were very small, say $\pm$ 2 percent, the difference in the costs would be very small and could be ignored. But if the errors of estimate can be very large, say 15 percent or more (and they are this large), the significance of error becomes very important, and the question as to which sort of error is preferable to make becomes a very important one. So far as we can judge, the prevailing opinion in Venezuela, as in most underdeveloped economies, is that it is better to make an error leading to excess steel capacity than an equal error leading to deficiency of capacity. We deal later with this view, in more detail, since it illustrates the importance of correct staging and phasing of expansion.

2.3 *The Optimality Criterion*

For purely private ventures, profit maximization based upon conventional accounting provides a basis of evaluation. For a public enterprise of the magnitude of the Orinoco Steel Plant, profit consideration, though important, is only one of many economic factors to be considered. As a state enterprise, it has substantial power to influence the central government to limit the amount of steel imports, and to place tariffs thereon. It can propose higher prices based upon its costs, and its costs may be high because of inefficiency. Proposals to increase capacity that is not profitable on the basis of import prices, may be made profit-

---

8. We assume for each of the four flat steel products, a zero error (i.e., as if our estimates were perfect), and three other error estimates.

able when import prices are increased by placing tariffs on them as in fact, one proposal for a tinning line submitted to the Corporación Venezolana de Guayana, suggested.

Since flat steel products are not produced in Venezuela, the only standard of comparison in assessing the decision to produce or import are the prices of imported flat steel products delivered to Venezuela. However, these prices vary considerably over time depending upon conditions in the steel exporting countries. This requires caution in using imported prices as a standard of comparison. We engaged in an analysis of the trends of prices from the major steel exporting countries to Venezuela, and concluded that the October, 1964, U.S.A. prices were a reasonable basis to use. We also used lower import prices as another alternative (i.e., one 90 percent of this level). To use maximum profits as an optimality criterion would require knowledge of the elasticity of demand with respect to price for each of the flat steel products for each year of the planning period (i.e., 15 to 20 years). Such information does not exist. If it did, we could incorporate it into the model, and could use profit as the objective to be maximized.

The previous considerations lead us to choose to minimize the total cost for the expected steel requirements over the planning period. However, as we are planning the total flat steel requirements of the Venezuelan economy over the planning period, we are subjected to the following constraint:

All domestic steel requirements of Venezuela will be met either through production of steel in Venezuela or by imports of steel into Venezuela.

This constraint appears to be in conformity with past and present Venezuelan practice and the high priority given by the Venezuelan government to industrial expansion, particularly in the engineering industries. A "domestic steel requirement" of Venezuela is the requirement of steel, as such, for any sector (including government itself) of the Venezuelan economy. Imports of steel, therefore, may always be viewed as an alternative to production of steel in Venezuela and hence to the installation of steel capacity. The optimality criterion therefore states: that steel expansion program is optimal which yields the lowest cost per ton, taking into consideration the costs of imports. Imports of steel are, thus, in our treatment, an alternative expansion "process" for every steel product. It is that process which has zero capital costs. Note that there is an important difference between the total discounted costs which we seek to minimize by correct choice of facility planning and that which a private entrepreneur selecting a steel plant seeks in minimizing costs. This comes about because of the contraint of meeting all steel requirements of the economy. A facility which is deficient in capacity in our definition has chargeable to it the cost of the necessary imported steel; a private entrepreneur would not, of course, view this as a cost of his facility. Thus, if we wish to minimize the total (discounted) costs of all steel expected to be required by the Venezuelan economy over the planning period, we must solve an optimal mix problem—that is to say, the least cost combination of local production and imports.

2.4   *The "Social" Cost of Steel Imports*

From the viewpoint of an individual importer of steel, the cost of steel imports is, in fact, what he actually pays for the steel delivered in Venezuela; i.e., the price per ton, plus transportation, insurance, etc. We term this the "private" cost of imported steel. From the point of view of Venezuela as a whole, it is urged that the "social" cost is this, plus something else. This "something else" refers to a social valuation, which holds that it is better to produce steel in Venezuela than to import it, even if imported steel is cheaper in the accounting or market price sense. It is often argued that since foreign exchange is scarce, any domestic production which conserves foreign exchange should be encouraged. Indeed, some have stated that this is the "most important justification" of all the possible reasons for encouraging local production of iron and steel.[9] For Venezuela, virtually all the major ingredients, other than equipment and high-grade coking coal are available locally, and significant amounts of foreign exchange may be saved through local production. A more general measure than foreign exchange might be the job creation potential of the marginal dollar invested within the country compared to expenditure for import goods of the same sort.

We shall term the cost, as a whole, of imported steel to the Venezuelan economy, the "social cost" of importing steel. This cost per ton of steel is essentially the import price plus a penalty factor which makes the social cost per ton rise, as volume of im-

Chart I

Private and Social Costs of Imported Steel

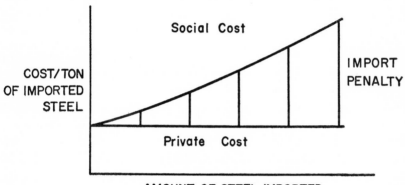

ported steel increases. Some weight is given to the import price of steel. This is as it should be, since if imported steel is very cheap compared to domestic steel, some imports may be advisable. On the other hand, by penalizing the import price as the volume of imports is increased (so that relative to local production imported steel becomes more expensive), weight is given to the social cost factor which, of course, also includes saving foreign

9. "The Iron and Steel Industry of Latin America—Plans and Perspectives," Steel Symposium, 1963, Discussion Paper. *ECLA*, 2, 30 October, 1963, 37. A foreign exchange savings optimality criterion; i.e., selecting that program which minimizes foreign exchange expenditures for steel products would fail without some cost criterion, since any capacity exceeding requirements would satisfy that criterion.

exchange expenditures for steel. The specific "penalty" we have chosen is, of course, arbitrary but has the desired property of increasing nonlinearly with volume of imports. Venezuelan authorities can set their own penalty estimates (including a zero penalty, which makes the social cost identical with the private cost as a negative penalty).[9a] The relationship between the private cost of imported steel and the social cost of imported steel is shown schematically in Chart I.

In our computations we will use both the private cost per ton and the social cost per ton to test the optimality of each alternative process (its capacity, number of stages, and timing of the stages). It is clear that if a particular expansion plan has a capacity much below the estimated demand, it incurs a heavy additional cost due to the large amount of imports required; on the other hand, if a particular plan has very much more capacity than estimated demand, it incurs no import penalty cost, but has a large cost of unutilized capacity. Our model takes this into account in determining the minimum expected discounted cost of each expansion possibility. The "import penalty," it should be noted, is not the same as varying the level of import prices. The latter does not vary with the amount of imports (on the reasonable assumption that the volume of imports of an underdeveloped country such as Venezuela is not large enough to seriously influence world export prices in steel). The import penalty varies with the volume of imports of Venezuela and is added on to the import price level.

One of the important reasons, in addition to national pride and similar noneconomic factors, which makes most underdeveloped economies prefer to produce even when imports are cheaper, is the experience during World War II of sharply curtailed steel imports to underdeveloped countries and Latin America in par-

---

9a. A more sophisticated and a correct measure of social cost would be the difference between import cost of steel less the value of indigenous output which could be produced with the resources saved by the import of steel. This could of course be positive or negative. If negative there is a positive benefit to importing steel. The problem with this measure is that short of a solution to the whole economy investment problem, it cannot be estimated correctly.

ticular (while they were selling raw materials at controlled prices to the U.S.A. and the West), and the sharp rises in steel prices after the war. Another economic reason which underdeveloped countries urge for producing their own steel where they have some favorable elements (such as iron ore or growing markets for steel primary products) even when imported steel is cheaper, is the belief that eventually they will also achieve economies of scale. Thus, they are willing to produce steel at prices higher than imports in the short run in the hope that growth of future markets for steel will allow them equal or lower prices in the future. If we relate these three considerations; i.e., foreign exchange savings, uncertainty of foreign steel supply, and future economies of scale, to the question previously raised—is it better in choosing a facility to err by choosing the higher capacity facility rather than the lower capacity facility—the clear preference is to choose the higher capacity facility.

2.5   *Steel Planning Strategies*

Three pure strategies exist for the steel planner attempting to relate steel capacity to demand for steel:

(a) Steel capacity over the planning period should be so planned that at any point in time within the planning period, it should always be substantially greater than demand.

(b) Steel capacity should be planned to be in approximate equilibrium with steel demand at any point in time.

(c)   Steel capacity should be planned to be substantially less than steel demand at any point in time. These strategic possibilities are shown schematically in Chart II.

2.6   *Comments on the Planning Strategies*

(a) *Capacity leading demand.* The first argument is that presence of surplus steel capacity is an inducement to steel using industries to expand beyond what they would do under conditions of just adequate capacity. This argument is supported by the following considerations:

First, steel prices will fall with steel surplus, which will increase the demand for steel; second, it will encourage import substitution of things made of steel; third, surplus steel capacity is necessary to allow steel-using sectors to expand. The effect of all these forces is to increase employment and presumably decrease foreign exchange expenditures. Whether all these things happen, of course, depends upon choosing the right (low price) policy for steel prices. It also depends upon the efficiency of the steel-using industries and their price polices. If the industries producing the things made of steel price these products above imports either because even with competitively priced steel inputs they still are less efficient and hence more costly than comparable imports or because of monopolistic power, the demand for steel would not necessarily increase since the demand for the steel-using products would not necessarily increase. On the other hand, the full extension of an import-substitution policy—in this case to steel and things made of steel—could have large income-increasing effects, which would swamp the negative price effects for some time at least.

(b) *Capacity just equal to demand.* It might seem that the ideal policy would plan to have steel capacity and steel demand in approximate equilibrium. This policy would minimize capital usage so that more capital is available for investment in other sectors; and to this extent it increases steel demand. Presumably, total unit costs in steel would be near their minimum at close to capacity operations. Shooting for such a target (assuming unbiased demand estimates) will lead to a pattern of occasional mild surplus or shortge. But in the latter case, output of steel-consuming industries is not restricted since steel can always be imported. Since the imports are small, foreign exchange expenditures for steel would also be low. If steel costs are a minimum under this policy and close to prices of steel imports, steel prices need not be lowered to stimulate steel demand. However, some of the arguments under (a) are not touched; i.e., there are dynamic considerations which favor some steel redundancy. Moreover, economies of scale may result in plant capacity which even though

Chart II

Patterns of Planning Steel Capacity

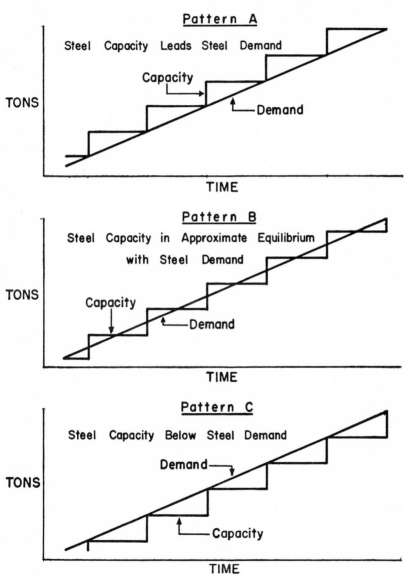

Pattern A

Steel Capacity Leads Steel Demand

Capacity

Demand

TONS

TIME

Pattern B

Steel Capacity in Approximate Equilibrium

with Steel Demand

Capacity

Demand

TONS

TIME

Pattern C

Steel Capacity Below Steel Demand

Demand

Capacity

TONS

TIME

not completely utilized may still yield lower total costs than smaller plants more completely utilized though total capital required would be greater. Clearly the size of the rate of interest and the extent of economies of scale are determining factors in this counter argument.

(c) *Capacity below demand.* Perhaps the most powerful argument in favor of this policy is that consideration of scale economies (in iron and steel production) forces a choice of either the policy of excess capacity or shortage of capacity. The policy of excess capacity builds to economic scale prior to the point where demand will fully utilize capacity. There is, therefore, a cost of unutilized capital. In a country suffering from capital deficiency this is a penalty upon total growth. The policy of under capacity allows demand to accumulate to the level of economic scale and then builds capacity to match. Demand can grow to this level by means of steel imports. Since world market prices in steel are likely to be no higher than Venezuelan prices, steel for the Venezuelan economy will always be available without penalty. This leads to saving of capital (compared to the surplus steel policy) which can be utilized in other industrial areas—e.g., in steel-*using* industries, or elsewhere. However, the validity of this argument depends upon the extent of economies of scale, the relative prices of imported steel and domestic steel, and the amount of foreign exchange available. It also ignores the possibility that some surplus steel capacity can be a stimulus to the expansion of steel-using industries.

Though each of the three planning patterns have some considerations in their favor, it is apparent that the choice depends upon quantitative considerations. The optimal strategy cannot be found by pure logic alone. Though any of the above "pure" strategies might turn out to be optimal on the basis of our analysis, it is also possible that a mixed situation will be optimal (in the sense of minimizing costs per ton of steel over the planning period)— that is, we are likely to find some interval during the planning period in which capacity is in excess of demand and some other interval in which it is deficient.[10] It is not necessary that the intervals be equal in duration or that the excess (of capacity) equal the deficiencies (of capacity). Moreover, we should note that to the extent that there is validity to the argument that surplus steel capacity (resulting from choosing larger capacity processes) is a demand-increasing factor, then the idea of a *social cost* of imports as we have treated it can be viewed as a convenient way of explicitly introducing this into the methodology of choice of alternative processes and their staging and phasing. Though the specific form and parameters of this penalty function are not known, even guesses on these serve a useful function by allowing explicit comparison of two optimal processes—one on the basis of a zero penalty, the other optimal when some penalty is used. It will show explicitly the difference in imports and thus foreign exchange expenditures of total output and employment within the industry, capital expenditures, and on total costs over the planning period of the two "optimal" choices.[11]

3. *Summary*

In our earlier article,[12] we have given in detail the model which permits us to choose the optimal steel expansion program from a list of alternative processes. This model selects the optimal staging and phasing of each alternative engineering plan. These facilities are capable of producing one or more products and the demand is known only subject to some probabalistic statement. In selecting the optimal program, the model determines optimal staging and phasing for each facility. The lowest cost of all these minimum cost stagings and phasings is the best program. We have defined the costs to also include, for each facility optimally staged and phased, the costs of such imports as would be necessary

10. The length of the planning period, as we have noted previously, will itself be an important factor influencing the choice of process, its staging, and the timing of its stages.

11. If one is lucky, the optimal process may be the same under zero and positive penalty. That is, it is possible that one process turns out to be so superior that even when imports are penalized it still is optimal with the same staging and phasing.

12. Sreedharan and Wein, *op. cit.*

each year if that facility were used. Therefore, the model solves also the best mix of imports of steel and local production for each alternative. We have indicated that if learning curves were known for each alternative facility this could be incorporated into the model. So, also, the problem of single plant optimal location, and the problem of optimal component size.

We do not wish to convey the impression that the construction of such a model is in any sense a substitute for judgment in economics, finance, engineering, and management, which are involved in the formulation and implementation of a sound steel expansion program. Nor do we wish to give the impression that computers have a magic by means of which right answers to complex problems automatically come forth. The model we have constructed depends upon judgment, upon knowledge of the advantages and disadvantages of various technical processes, and upon information. If our judgments, knowledge, and information are inadequate, the answer given by the model will be wrong. But the strength of the model, together with the computational powers of the computer, lies in the fact that an explicit, analytical method is given, whereby, with better judgment, knowledge, and information many more alternatives can be examined simultaneously and the best one selected. The model thus becomes a powerful tool to supplement management judgment.

A complete expansion program will include management, operations, and financial planning. This paper deals with only one basic aspect of a comprehensive steel expansion program— the economic-engineering aspect. It provides a method which determines optimally how much product capacity is required, what basic equipment should be used, and when it should be installed. The large gains or losses in any investment program depend upon the solutions of these questions.

In the following chapter, we give a simplified mathematical model.

Chapter III

A Simplified Mathematical Analysis

1. *The Mathematics of the Model*

Below we shall point out some of the conceptual parts of the mathematical technique underlying the model without being complete or going into the details. For a detailed exposition we refer the reader to the Appendix I where our article is reprinted. As indicated earlier we use the functional equation technique of dynamic programming. For the reader's convenience, we wish to make the derivation of the equations given below self-contained (at least at the conceptual stage). Hence, we shall briefly review the functional equation technique of dynamic programming as applied to an optimization problem. Our discussion will be lined up so that it directly applies to our present problem.

2. *Dynamic Programming*

Suppose we seek the supremum (maximum) of a real-valued bounded function f defined on a cartesian product $X_1 \times X_2$ of two spaces. We shall let X_2 depend on the first coordinate x_1: we display this by writing $X_2(x_1)$. Then

$$(1) \qquad \sup_{(x_1,x_2)\epsilon X_1 \times X_2(x_1)} f(x_1,x_2) = \sup_{x_1\epsilon X_1} \sup_{x_2\epsilon X_2(x_1)} f(x_1,x_2)$$

But now suppose that the special analytic nature of f is such that f is "separable," then we would have found the solution of the original problem (the left of eq(1)) in terms of the two simpler problems (the right of eq (1)). We may iterate this method a finite number of times when the function is defined on a cartesian product of n spaces, each space itself depending on the preceding choice of variables in a simple manner.

3. *An Example*

Let us illustrate this idea by an example (probably the simplest example illustrating the idea) given in Bellman's *Dynamic Programming*, Princeton University Press, 1957, pp. 40-41 as a problem.

The problem is to maximize the product function $F^{(n)}$ of n variables defined by

(2) $F^{(n)}(t_1, \ldots, t_n) = t_1 t_2 \ldots t_n$

subject to the constraints

(3) $t_1 + \ldots + t_n = T > O, t_i \geqq O, i = 1, \ldots, n;$

where $T > O$ is given. We shall abbreviate by Δ_n the constraint set defined by (3). Writing

(4) $f_n(T) = \max_{\Delta_n} F^{(n)}(t_1, \ldots, t_n)$

we see that

(5) $\max F^{(n)}(t_1, \ldots, t_n) = \max_{\substack{O \leqq t_n \leqq T}} \max_{\substack{t_i \geqq O \\ t_1 + \ldots t_{n-1} = T-t_n}} F^{(n)}(t, \ldots, t_n).$

Noting

(6) $F^{(n)}(t_1, \ldots, t_n) = t_n F^{(n-1)}(t_1, \ldots, t_{n-1})$

and using definition (4) we get

$$\max_{\substack{t_i \geqq O \\ t_1 + \ldots + t_{n-1} = T-t_n}} F^{(n)}(t_1, \ldots, t_n) = t_n f_{n-1}(T-t_n).$$

Hence (5) becomes

(7) $f_n(T) = \max_{0 \le t_n \le T} t_n f_{n-1}(T-t_n),$

or

(8) $f_n(T) = \max_{0 \le t \le T} t f_{n-1}(T-t).$

Note that in this case $f_1(T)$ is clearly given by

(9) $f_1(T) = \max_{0 \le t_1 \le T} t_1 = T.$

Hence from (8)

(10) $f_2(T) = \max_{0 \le t \le T} t f_1(T-t)$

$$= \max_{0 \le t \le T} t(T-t) = \frac{T^2}{4}$$

Now, we can use (8) again to find f_3, then repeating the process we find f_4, and by iteration we get to f_n.

In this special problem a simple mathematical induction will yield the explicit solution

(11) $f_n(T) = \frac{T^n}{n^n},$

which is not our primary concern.

This problem illustrates two of the most fundamental aspects of dynamic programming: to wit, one attempts to reduce an n dimensional problem to a sequence of n, one-dimensional problems; this attempt will be fruitful *only if* the function is "separable," for example like (6) above.

As one builds up the sequence of functions $f_1, \ldots, f_n$ we can find the points where the maxima of each function occurs, e.g., $t_n^*(T)$ for $f_n(T)$ defined by

(12) $f_n(T) = t_n^*(T) f_{n-1}(T-t_n^*(T))$

The optimal values of $t_n, \ldots, t_1$ will then be given by $t_n^*(T),$

$t_{n-1}^*(T-t_n^*(T))$, $t_{n-2}^*(T-t_n^*(T) - t_{n-1}^*(T-t_n^*(T)))$, etc., in the reverse order, since we will start with the nth stage and work backwards via the functional equation (8).

4. *Mathematical Analysis of the Model*

Recall that we wish to time the stages of a process so that the total cost (expected cost, actually) is a minimum during a fixed planning horizon. We denote the planning horizon by T, the total number of stages of the process by n, and the times when they are put in by $t_1, t_2, \ldots, t_n$; where t_i corresponds to the time when the i-th stage begins. The first stage must precede the second, the second must precede the third, etc., so that we have

$$(13) \quad 0 \leq t_1 \leq \ldots \leq t_n \leq T.$$

The possible equalities in the above allow for simultaneous initiation of certain stages.

We work out the total cost for a process assuming the timing to be $(t_1, t_2, \ldots, t_n)$, i.e., write down the function $F^{(n)}(t_1, \ldots, t_n)$ representing the total expected cost. Once we have such an expression we seek the minimum of $F^{(n)}(t_1, \ldots, t_n)$ subject to the constraint $0 \leq t_1 \leq \ldots \leq t_n \leq T$. Due to the specific nature of this function $F^{(n)}(t_1, \ldots, t_n)$, it will turn out that the dynamic programming procedure of Bellman would be applicable to an intermediate function of n variables, which is to be introduced appropriately. This then yields the optimal timing $(t_1^*, \ldots, t_n^*)$ of the n stages and the corresponding cost. The whole procedure being algorithmic there is no great difficulty in translating the above procedure into one of the algebraic languages used in a modern digital computer. Of course, one adds to the computer routine many other subroutines which give the standard accounting type information regarding imports, operating costs, operational levels, etc. Then the computer simply compares the total costs figures of each process and selects the one with the least cost.

Let us be more specific about the function $F^{(n)}(t_1, \ldots, t_n)$. We shall assume a discounting rate α and salvage rate β. At stage i the capital invested will be denoted by K_i. Since we are considering a multi-product process, the capacity for j-th product in the i-th stage will be denoted by ρ_{ij}. We shall break the operating costs into two components: d_{ij} per unit of capacity and c_{ij} per unit of output of the j-th product at the i-th stage. Then there are the demand functions $d_j(t)$, these being the demand rates for j-th product at time t. Note, however, in our formulation the parameters defining $d_j(t)$ are only known stochastically. Now the available capacity at the i-th stage for the j-th product may be less than the demand for the j-th product at the i-th stage. We are then assuming the difference would be made up by importing at certain delivered import prices M_j. Naturally, we assume that even if capacity permits one will not produce more than the demand for the product at that time. The function $F^{(n)}(t_1, t_2, \ldots, t_n)$ is simply a closed analytic expression (though cumbersome), representing the total expected cost of the process if we choose a timing policy $(t_1, \ldots, t_n)$ all costs being calculated on a present-worth basis with a planning horizon equal to T.

The intermediate function $G^{(n)}$ alluded to earlier turns out to be essential to apply the functional equation technique of dynamic programming: for, the original $F^{(n)}$ is not readily separable, whereas, $G^{(n)}$ is. So we have the equations

$$(14) \quad F^{(n)}(t_1, \ldots, t_n) = G^{(n)}(t_1, \ldots, t_n) + \phi(t_n, T)$$

and

$$(15) \quad G^{(n)}(t_1, \ldots, t_n) = G^{(n-1)}(t_1, \ldots, t_{n-1}) + \psi_{n-1}(t_{n-1}, t_n)$$

where the function $G^{(n)}$ and ψ_{n-1} are defined by (14) and (15). The definition would be complete if we write out $F^{(n)}$ and ϕ explicitly. In fact, we have

$$F^{(n)}(t_1, \ldots, t_n) = \sum_{i=1}^{n} K_i [\exp(-\alpha t_i) - \exp\{-(\beta + \alpha)T + \beta t_i\}]$$

$$+ E\left(\sum_{j=1}^{p}\left[M_j \int_{0}^{t_1} \{\mu d_j(t) + \lambda d_j^2(t)\} \exp(-\alpha t) dt\right.\right.$$

$$(16) \quad + \sum_{i=1}^{n} \int_{t_i}^{t_{i+1}} \{c_{ij}r_{ij}(t) + d_{ij}\rho_{ij}$$

$$+ M_j[\mu(d_j(t) - r_{ij}(t)) + \lambda(d_j(t) - r_{ij}(t))^2]\} \exp(-\alpha t)dt\Big]\Big)$$

and

$$\phi(t_n,T) = K_n[\exp(-\alpha t_n) - \exp(-(\beta + \alpha)T + \beta t)]$$

$$(17) \quad + E\Big(\sum_{j=1}^{p} \int_{t_n}^{T} \{c_{nj}\, r_{nj}(t) + d_{nj}\rho_{nj}$$

$$+ M_j[\mu(d_j(t) - r_{nj}(t)) + \lambda(d_j(t) - r_{nj}(t))^2]\} \exp(-\alpha t)dt\Big),$$

where $t_{n+1} = T$.

Here $r_{ij}(t)$ is the actual output rate at time t of the j-th product in the i-th stage of the process. The costs of the imports are permitted to vary non-linearly to incorporate social costs. This explains the coefficients μ and λ. Note that the expectation operator E in (16) and (17) is needed since r_{ij} and d_j are only known stochastically.

We also write

$$(18) \quad f(n,T) = \min_{0 \le t_1 \le \ldots \le t_n \le T} F^{(n)}(t_1, \ldots, t_n)$$

and

$$(19) \quad g(n,\tau) = \min_{0 \le t_1 \le \ldots \le t_{n-1} \le \tau} G^{(n)}(t_1, \ldots, t_n)$$

From these we get the recursion relations

$$(20) \quad f(n,T) = \min_{0 \le t \le \tau} \{g(n,t) + \phi(t,T)\}$$

and

$$(21) \quad g(n,\tau) = \min_{0 \le t \le \tau} \} g(n-1,t) + \psi_{n-1}(t,\tau)\}$$

with the boundary conditions

$$(22) \quad g(1,r) = E \left(\sum_{j=1}^{p} M_j \int_0^r \{\mu d_j(t) + \lambda d_j^2(t)\} \exp(-\alpha t) dt \right).$$

We shall not go into the rest of the details involved in actually evaluating the above equations using a digital computer and analytical techniques. For these the reader is again referred to Appendix I.

Chapter IV

Substantive Results — The Venezuelan Case

1. *Background Information*

Developing a steel industry in an underdeveloped country, even a relatively rich one such as Venezuela, is a risky undertaking. Huge sums of capital are required. Venezuela has already invested close to $400 million in the present Orinoco Plant. Expansion of this plant to produce flat steel products could easily add another $300 million; and even this expansion must be followed by others of equal expense to augment its basic raw steel capacity. The direct employment given by this plant is small compared to the capital invested per worker. As of 1965, about 5,000 workers were employed (and these were too many) in the Orinoco Plant, which resulted in a capital investment of about $80,000 per man. The plant was then operating at about 60 percent of capacity. Even at capacity it would employ about 7,500 workers or about $54,000 capital investment per man. This figure does not include the investment in a relatively small hydro-electric plant (360,000 KW) which cost $60 million, and which was used virtually entirely to supply the Orinoco Plant with power.[1] One must have great faith in the multiplier effect of steel production to justify such enormous capital expenditures per man employed.

---

1. The Orinoco Plant had very large power use for a plant of its size because the iron producing furnaces were electric smelting furnaces of Norwegian design.

These kinds of expenditures should place great pressure upon the planners. Unfortunately, the charisma of steel expansion is so great that much less is done than could be done even with the relatively poor information which is available.

Our specific task for the C.V.G. was to recommend the kind, capacity, and phasing of a flat steel products expansion to be undertaken at Orinoco. It was not to judge, given all the alternatives in other sectors and the overall planning of Venezuelan Government, whether a flat steel products expansion should be undertaken. As it turned out, two studies were made, one of the operations of the Orinoco Steel Plant (previously footnoted) and the other, an evaluation of the flat products expansion. On the basis of the first report (1964) we recommended that no expansion of flat products be undertaken until clear evidence was available to show that the work force, (managerial, manual, and technical) was able to operate the present facilities at normal efficiencies. As of the report date, the Orinoco Plant had been under operation for four years and was far from achieving normal efficiencies in most of its departments. Our recommendation was accepted. The second report, completed in April, 1965, used a planning period starting in 1969, which would be the first full year for which a steel expansion program undertaken in 1965 could be operational.

2. *Demand Estimates*

Demand estimates are, of course, the first item to be determined in planning a steel expansion program. The then current Plan de la Nación (1963-1966) called for an annual rate of growth of 8 percent in G.N.P. In five basic sectors heavily influencing steel requirement, the estimated growth rates were as follows:

Sector	Annual Rate of Growth
Electricity, gas and water	18.0%
Construction	14.9%
Manufacturing	13.5%
Agricultural production	7.9%
Petroleum	4.0%

Of course, such figures were target estimates, they extended only to 1966, and we had to estimate demand through at least 1983. Moreover, they said nothing about steel, to wit, four kinds of steel —plates, hot rolled sheets, cold rolled sheets, and tin plates; further, width and thickness information is needed to really plan a steel mill. Two estimates were available to us: one made by two U.S.A. economic consultants based upon American usage as given in the *Census of Manufactures* and expressed as broad industrial aggregates, i.e., tons of steel per $1000 of output in construction, in electrical machinery, in transportation equipment, and so forth and extrapolated to 1980 on the basis of essentially judgmental rates of growth. The other was made by a prominent U.S. engineering firm long experienced in steel plant design and construction. These estimates were made by free hand extrapolations of time trends—and, of course, judgment. The figures were miles apart. For all flat products in 1980, for example, the engineering firm estimated apparent steel consumption of 772,000 tons; the economic consultants estimated 1,684,000 tons.[2] The differences in the specific steel products were even greater in percentages. To obtain some notion of the upper and lower limits of what purely statistical techniques of trend analysis would reveal, we used a linear function of time and a log linear on the past data. These least squares estimates also had a useful by-product in giving us, also, some idea of the variance in estimates of the future based upon the past trends.

After careful analysis of these four estimates and analysis of the Plan de la Nación, of the rates of growth of other underdeveloped countries with steel industries, of the relationship between hot and cold rolled sheets as illustrated by U.S. experience, we formed our own estimates.[3] These estimates are given in Table

---

2. This was our revision of their estimates, which included also exports from Venezuela and all steel contained in things made of steel, to make it comparable to "apparent steel consumption," i.e., steel production plus steel imports minus steel exports.

3. For the details of this, see H. Wein, V. P. Sreedharan, P. Maal, "Optimal Expansion of Flat Steel Products," Part II, Technical Report, pp. 50-89, and Appendix I and II, pp. 1-34.

TABLE I

*Comparison of Estimated Apparent Consumption of
Flat Products—Venezuela 1966-1980*
(000 Metric Tons)

Product	Actual 1963	1966	1970	1975	1980
Plates	17				
Linear-Least Squares (L.S.)		28	32	37	41
Engineering Consultant		21	28	40	59
This Report		35	55	97	156
Economic Consultant		96	165	288	445
Log-Linear Least Squares (L.L.S.)		28	36	50	69
Hot Rolled Sheets	24**				
L. S.		n.a.	n.a.	n.a.	n.a.
Engineerng Consultant		64	99	145	213
This Report		71	125	224	332
Economic Consultant		84	148	252	485
L. L. S.		n.a.	n.a.	n.a.	n.a.
Cold Rolled Sheets	43**				
L. S.		n.a.	n.a.	n.a.	n.a.
Engineering Consultant		79	136	215	346
This Report		88	188	365	616
Economic Consultant		37	76	144	353
L. L. S.		n.a.	n.a.	n.a.	n.a.
Total Sheets	67				
L. S.		83	103	128	153
Engineering Consultant		143	235	360	559
This Report		159	313	589	948
Economic Consultant		121	224	396	838
L. L. S.		159	333	840	2121
Tin Plate	53				
L. S.	53	67	82	102	121
Engineering Consultant		64	86	115	154
This Report		84	106	142	190
"Estudio"		84	110	143	187
Economic Consultant		96	148	256	401
L. L. S.		92	161	322	644
All Flats	137				
L. S.		177	217	266	315
Engineering Consultant		228	349	515	772
This Report		278	474	828	1294
Economic Consultant		313	537	940	1684
L. L. S.		278	496	1019	2094

**Estimated.

I. "This Report" estimates in Table I are our estimates under zero variance and for the rates of growth we think are most likely. The terms "L.S."and "L.L.S." refer to linear and log linear least squares projections. Chart III perhaps more clearly reveals the spread of the estimates for total flats. Our best estimate lies somewhat below the two highest; our low estimate is somewhat lower than the engineering firm's estimate but much above the extrapolation of the least squares linear time trend. The rates of growth for the flat steel products are shown in Table II.

TABLE II

Mean Annual Growth Rates of Flat Products—Best Estimate
(percent)

	1963-1970	1970-1975	1975-1983
Total Sheets	18.5	13.5	10.0
Tin Plate	6.0	6.0	6.0
Plate	12.0	12.0	10.0

Mean Annual Growth Rates of Flat Products—Low Estimate
(percent)

	1963-1970	1970-1975	1975-1983
Cold Rolled Sheets	15.0	10.0	8.0
Hot Rolled Sheets	14.0	9.0	7.0
Plates	10.0	8.0	6.0
Tin Plate	6.0	5.0	4.5

Errors in the Demand Estimates. The analysis is probabalistic, i.e., the mean rates of growth of each of the four products are assumed to be subject to error. These errors are measured in terms of the standard deviation. Three possibilities are given— "realistic" estimates of error (what we really expect), optimistic estimates (if we are lucky), and pessimistic estimates (if we go haywire). The fourth is the certainty case—used as a bench-mark—in which the mean rates of growth for each product are assumed to have zero standard deviation, i.e., no error. These

CHART III

Comparison of Different Demand Estimates of Total Flats, 1966-1980

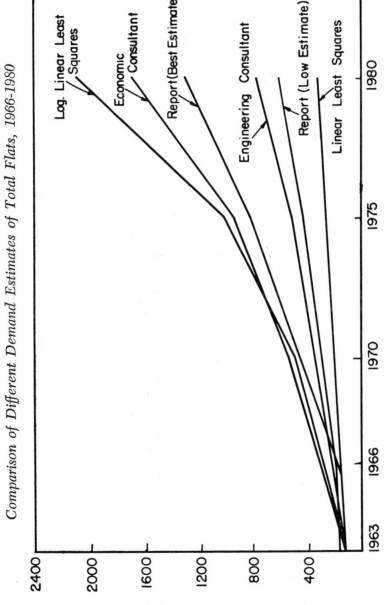

TABLE III

Estimates of Standard Deviation of Mean Growth Rates

Percent of the Mean Growth Rate

	Realistic	Pessimistic	Optimistic
Cold Rolled Sheets	12	30	6
Hot Rolled Sheets	12	30	6
Plates	15	30	10
Tin Plate	10	30	5

"errors" are given for both the best estimate and the low estimate of demand. They are as follows:

We have assumed normal distributions (although as we have shown in our full mathematical paper, other distributions could also be used) at the cost of somewhat more computation.[4]

These rather large differences in estimates over a fifteen- or twenty-year time period we believe are inevitable for any country including those completely planned (so long as they are willing to deviate from plans). Their significance for the problem of choice, that is to say, the problem of optimal staging and phasing of alternative processes, is that it forces consideration of a wider variety of alternative processes. It specifically should bring to the planner's attention the possibilities involved in staging, and move him to consider the various alternative stagings that are feasible for each process alternative. Unless one has devised the feasible alternatives and actually put them to the test of evaluation, it is not possible to know whether the possible variation of errors made in the demand estimates will significantly change the result. If it turns out that the choice is significantly different depending upon which demand estimate is used, the alternative is either to wait for better information, or to formulate a decision criterion such as minimizing the greatest risk or other decision criteria that will guide one to a single estimate. In the present case, the large differences between all the estimates, including our own *best* and *low* estimates, indicated that a wide spectrum

---

4. Wein, Sreedharan, and Mall, *op. cit.*, p. 54, fn. 3.

of possible processes had to be evaluated. Though we could eliminate the estimates other than our own as poorly founded, we could not objectively state that the evidence for our best estimate was stronger than our low estimate; and between these two, many possible plants could be designed.

3. *The Process Alternatives*

Eight basic technological alternatives capable of producing some or all of the flat steel products were examined. The two lowest capacity processes, the mechanized sheet and tin plate mill and the Steckel hot mills with reversing cold mills were found to be inferior to all other processes at the conditions most favorable to these low capacity processes; viz., the lowest demand estimate at all levels of error, and the highest import prices at zero social cost penalty. It was, therefore, unnecessary to test them further. This left six feasible processes and one proposal to construct a tin plate mill without other facilities. The six basic processes include:

(a) Two semi-continuous hot mills with reversing cold mills. One of these is the International Construction Company's Alternative I, which employs a Sendzimir cold mill.[5]

(b) Three semi-continuous hot mills with tandem cold mills— these differ from each other in their annual capacity in the particular flat products. Two of these are so planned that they can be linked; i.e., the smaller capacity process can be expanded to the larger.

(c) A fully continuous hot mill with tandem cold mills. All of these include electrolytic tin plate capacity and corrugating and galvanizing facilities for sheets.

3.1. *Staging and Integration.*

Staging

Twenty-six different combinations of installing the six basic methods were tested plus one other possibility which is the in-

---

5. This is a British firm of Consulting Engineers which had submitted an engineering plan based upon estimates of demand which had been given to them.

stallation of tinning capacity as a beginning stage—making a total of twenty-seven alternatives. The combinations include technologically compatible staging of the different processes, and systematic testing of different degrees of integration—i.e., testing the costs of buying different metallic inputs from abroad, or making them in Venezuela. The staging consists of five possibilities:

(a) *Single Stage.* The full capacity of the process is installed at one time. That is to say, the full complement of equipment, buildings, and ancillary service facilities are installed during one period of continuous construction.

(b) *Cold Mill Staging.* The process is installed in pieces, with cold mills installed first, since they produce the most valuable products; i.e., cold rolled sheets, tin plate, and galvanized sheets. At some later time when demand warrants, the hot mills necessary to complete the process are installed. Construction is thus broken into two periods. Production of the cold products proceeds on the basis of the importation of hot rolled coils. If it is contemplated that hot mills will eventually be installed, provision is made for them in the initial planning and construction, in order to minimize both construction and production interruption expenses. Thus necessary foundations, piling, etc., for the hot mill stage is provided in the cold mill stage. Construction costs for multiple staging are always higher than in single staging for the same process.

(c) *Hot Mill Staging.* Hot mills are installed to produce the coils for the cold mills and to produce finished hot rolled sheets and plates, and finished hot rolled coils sold as such. When hot mills are installed, the process is completed, and the full range and capacity of the process is capable of being attained in each product.

(d) *Combination Staging.* Combination staging occurs when two technologically compatible processes each of which can produce a full range of products (i.e., cold rolled sheets, hot rolled sheets, plates and tin plates), and each of which can be broken into cold mill and hot mill stages, are linked. Thus, in effect, the last staging of the linked processes completes a process which could have been built single stage. The potential advantage of such combination staging as opposed to single staging of the component processes (or multiple staging of the component processes), is that capacity can more nearly match demand at the time when it is needed. Thus combination staging can obtain the advantages of capacity staging and product staging, such as is involved in the installation of cold mills first, then hot mills.

(e) *Tin Plate Staging.* This is a staging which breaks cold mill staging into two substages: (1) install electrolytic tinning facilities only, and (2) install the cold mills. When the electrolytic tinning facilities are installed, cold rolled coils ready for tinning must be imported. Eventually the cold mills are installed. Our computer analysis revealed that no matter which basic process was used (for cold mills), it was always cheaper over the fifteen-year planning period to install cold mills and electrolytic tinning facilities simultaneously. This conclusion held also for all levels of demand tested.

Integration

The largest single cost in producing any of the flat rolled products is the cost of the metallic input. The metallic input varies depending upon the stage of the process. Thus the metallic inputs are as follows:

Stage	Metallic Input
Electrolytic Tinning	Cold reduced, annealed, tempered coils
Cold Mills	Hot rolled coils
Hot Mills	Slabs
Slabbing Mills	Ingots
Ingots	Hot iron and scrap
Hot Iron	Iron ore, sinter, scale

For each stage the metallic input can be either produced in the same plant (or elsewhere in Venezuela) or imported from abroad, or some combination of the two when capacity is not balanced in all the stages. When the hot mills of a flat rolling process are fully supplied by slabs made in the same plant, and the slabs are made from ingots which are made in the same plant, we say that the flat process is "fully integrated." We designate this degree of integration by the number "1." When slabs are imported for the hot mills rather than made in a fully integrated process, we designate this degree of integration by the number "2"; when hot rolled coils are imported, we use the number "3" to designate the degree of integration, and when cold rolled coils are imported (as in electrolytic tinning as a stage), we use the number "4."[6]

Clearly one of the basic alternatives which must be evaluated in the choice of a flat rolling process is which degree of integration is optimal—that is to say, least costly given the estimated demand over the planning period. This "degree of integration" includes also which staging is optimal and thus can include different degrees of integration at different stages and hence different times. The twenty-seven alternatives tested thus involve systematic comparisons of the six basic flat rolling processes in different degrees of staging and integration. These are shown in Table IV.

TABLE IV

Index of Process Alternatives Tested

Computer Name of Alternative (Process)	Description	No. of Stages	Degree of Integra- tion	Total Invest- ment (Millions B's)	Annual Capacity (000 Tons)			
					(1) C.R.S.	(2) H.R.S.	(3) P.	(4) T.P.
1	S.C.-RCM	1	1	692.7	166	63	92	115
2	S.C.-RCM-ICC I	1	1	645.8	155	115	92	130
3	S.C.-TCM (1)	1	1	673.2	230	173	75	115
4	S.C.-TCM (2)	1	1	884.1	368	97	138	130
5	S.C.-TCM (3)	1	1	1271.2	403	288	230	230
6	C-TCM	1	1	1843.0	1000	450	250	350
7	S.C.-RCM	2	3,1	708.6				
	C.M.	3		238.8	166	0	0	115
	H.M.	1		469.8	166	63	92	115

6. We have omitted the possibility of purchasing ingots from abroad to be rolled into slabs at Orinoco, because analysis of the import prices of slabs and ingots compared to operating costs at even standard efficiencies of rolling these purchased ingots into slabs at Orinoco revealed that it was cheaper to import slabs than to import ingots to be rolled into slabs.

TABLE IV *(Cont.)*

Computer Name of Alternative (Process)	Description	No. of Stages	Degree of Integration	Total Investment (Millions B's)	(1) C.R.S.	(2) H.R.S.	(3) P.	(4) T.P.
8	S.C.-RCM-ICC I	2	3,1	658.6				
		C.M.	3	198.0	155	0	0	130
		H.M.	1	460.6	155	115	92	130
9	S.C.-TCM (1)	2	3,1	687.1				
		C.M.	3	196.3	230	0	0	115
		H.M.	1	490.8	230	173	75	115
10	S.C.-TCM (2)	2	3,1	906.1				
		C.M.	3	281.0	368	0	0	130
		H.M.	1	625.1	368	97	138	130
11	S.C.-TCM (3)	2	3,1	1301.6				
		C.M.	3	399.0	403	0	0	230
		H.M.	1	902.6	403	288	230	230
12	S.C.-RCM	2	3,2	438.4				
		C.M.	3	238.8	166	0	0	115
		H.M.	2	199.6	166	63	92	115
13	S.C.-RCM-ICC I	2	3,2	362.5				
		C.M.	3	198.0	155	0	0	130
		H.M.	2	164.5	155	115	92	130
14	S.C.-TCM (1)	2	3,2	357.9				
		C.M.	3	196.3	230	0	0	115
		H.M.	2	161.9	230	173	75	230
15	S.C.-TCM (2)	2	3,2	513.1				
		C.M.	3	281.0	368	0	0	130
		H.M.	2	232.1	368	97	138	130
16	S.C.-TCM (3)	2	3,2	729.3				
		C.M.	3	399.0	403	0	0	230
		H.M.	2	330.3	403	288	230	230
17	S.C.-TCM	2	1,1	1271.2				
		C.M.+ H.M.	1	673.2	230	173	75	115
		C.M.+ H.M.	1	598.0	403	288	230	230
18	S.C.-TCM	4	3,1,3,1	1301.6				
		C.M.	3	196.3	230	0	0	115
		H.M.	1	490.8	230	173	75	115
		C.M.	3	202.7	403	173	75	230
		H.M.	1	411.8	403	288	230	230
19	S.C.-TCM	3	1,3,1	1287.7				
		C.M.+ H.M.	1	673.2	230	173	75	115

TABLE IV (Cont.)

Computer Name of Alternative (Process)	Description	No. of Stages	Degree of Integration	Total Investment (Millions B's)	Annual Capacity (000 Tons)			
					(1) C.R.S.	(2) H.R.S.	(3) P.	(4) T.P.
	C.M.	3	3	202.7	403	173	75	230
	H.M.	1	1	411.8	403	288	230	230
20	S.C.-TCM	3	3,3,1	1300.6				
	C.M.	3	3	196.3	230	0	0	115
	C.M.	3	3	202.7	403	0	0	230
	H.M.	1	1	901.6	403	288	230	230
21	S.C.-TCM	2	3,1	1301.6				
	C.M.	3	3	196.3	230	0	0	115
	C.M.+ H.M.	1	1	1105.3	403	288	230	230
22	S.C.-TCM	2	2,2	698.9				
	C.M.+ H.M.	2	2	344.3	230	173	75	115
	C.M.+ H.M.	2	2	354.6	403	288	230	230
23	S.C.-TCM	4	3,2,3,2	729.3				
	C.M.	3	3	196.3	230	0	0	115
	H.M.	2	2	161.9	230	173	75	115
	C.M.	3	3	202.7	403	173	75	230
	H.M.	2	2	168.4	403	288	230	230
24	S.C.-TCM	3	2,3,2	715.4				
	C.M.+ H.M.	2	2	344.3	230	173	75	115
	C.M.	3	3	202.7	403	173	75	230
	H.M.	2	2	168.4	403	288	230	230
25	S.C.-TCM	3	3,3,2	728.3				
	C.M.	3	3	196.3	230	0	0	115
	C.M.	3	3	202.7	403	0	0	230
	H.M.	2	2	329.3	403	288	230	230
26	S.C.-TCM	2	3,2	698.9				
	C.M.	3	3	196.3	230	0	0	115
	C.M.+ H.M.	2	2	502.6	403	288	230	230
27	Tinning	2	4,4	93.8				
	Tinning	4	4	46.9	0	0	0	135
	Tinning	4	4	93.9	0	0	0	270

Key: S.C.   = Semi-Continuous Hot Mills
      RCM   = Reversing Cold Mills
      RCM-ICC I   = International Construction Company Alternative I
      TCM   = Tandem Cold Mills
      C   = Continuous Hot Mills

C.M.   = Cold Mills including electrolytic tin plate
H.M.   = Hot Mills

Notes to Table II:

Degree of Integration (1) = Completely integrated; iron, steel and slabs made at Orinoco using L.D. steel furnaces, electric pig iron furnaces and 1100 m.m. mill for slabs.

           (2) = Slabs are purchased for the hot mills; that is, imported.

           (3) = Hot rolled coils are imported for the cold mills.

           (4) = Cold reduced coils are imported for electrolytic tinning.

4. Cost Information

For all these twenty-seven alternatives, cost information was required. This cost information included the capital cost of the equipment, the construction cost corresponding to each of the alternatives, the variable operating costs based upon standard physical inputs converted into money costs using Venezuelan prices, and the labor inputs broken into managerial, technical, and operating labor (including maintenance labor) per shift. The labor inputs were taken at standard efficiencies, i.e., the labor required in developed steel making nations for comparable plants. These were also converted into money costs at Venezuelan wage and salary levels including the government contribution for fringe benefits. A further breakdown was made with labor inputs into crews required per shift, and the various classes of labor. The distinction between truly variable inputs such as electrical energy, steam, and metallics, and "semi-variable" such as almost all the labor inputs which varied with shift rather than proportionately to output was also made. The cost of imported metallic inputs were taken at the two levels of import prices already mentioned.

Every effort was made to obtain cost information on all foreseeable cost items. Nevertheless prior to actual operation of a plant exact operating costs cannot be obtained. However, this is an insuperable difficulty. All that can be done in this regard is to avoid methods which contain bias, which would distort the relative position of the different processes. The one bias actually not avoided is the bias resulting from taking the operating costs at their standard levels for each process. This bias in the processes we evaluated would be most pronounced in the two smallest capacity processes, which as we indicated were eliminated after preliminary evaluation under conditions most favorable to these processes. Nevertheless, there would still be some differences in the rate at which the remaining processes could be mastered— knowledgeable operating engineers whom we consulted estimated this to be one year at the outside. That is, the most difficult process of all that we considered would take one year more than the least difficult, and the most difficult would take about three years to bring Venezuelan personnel up to standard efficiency. Under these circumstances we ignored the possibility of actually incorporating learning curve information—since these would add to the programming complications and in any case these learning curves were not known in detail for each of the processes. We had the option once the optimal process of the 27 examined was known, to reconsider whether the extent of this bias could significantly change the results. If so, we could attempt to get better information on this point. As it turned out, we did not have to engage in this further information task.

As we have mentioned, the capital costs would also not be known exactly for each process until actual bids were solicited. Nevertheless, as all the processes were well known, fairly reliable prices were available and no bias from that source could be seen. The major difficulty in estimating capital costs were those involved in construction of each of the twenty-seven alternatives. But here also no precise information can be obtained until bids are solicited. But again those experienced in steel plant construction can estimate these costs for the different processes examined. Though the error is likely to be greater than in estimating equipment costs, there was no reason to believe that they would be biased with respect to alternative processes. These practical difficulties do not vitiate the logic of the model, but they are necessary to properly interpret the results. As a practical matter it is not feasible to obtain twenty-seven detailed bids from engineering and construction firms. But if serious question remains after the evaluation based upon the estimated costs, sensitivity analysis could be resorted to—a directed sensitivity analysis on the costs— or several, say the best three processes could be let out for bid, more precise information obtained, and the three alternatives re-evaluated.

5. *Parameter Alternatives*

The parameter alternatives we had to consider were:

(a) *The rate of interest on the net capital each year.* The rate of interest is to be interpreted in its economic sense as the marginal efficiency of capital rather than the rate at which the Venezuelan Government could procure capital. This latter figure was then less than 6 percent. We decided upon three values of this opportunity cost of capital as embracing the range: 6 percent, 9 percent, and 12 percent. Most Venezuelan economists believed the true opportunity rate to be about 9 percent.

(b) *The capital usage each year.* After discussion with operating executives of the Orinoco plant we set this at 6 percent per year to a residual salvage value of 10 percent of initial capital outlay.

(c) *Labor rates* were taken at January, 1965, levels of the Orinoco plant, including the Government fringe benefits.

(d) *Import prices* of steel products were set at October, 1964, U.S.A. f.o.b. prices to which were added the transportation costs to La Guaira or Matanzas (the steel plant location) depending upon which was relevant; the transportation costs included all associated costs, i.e., insurance, loading and unloading, etc.

(e) *Social costs* were taken at zero penalty and a particular level of positive penalty.

(f) *Demand estimates* were taken at our "best level" and "low level" estimates, together with four levels of variance, i.e., the realistic, pessimistic, optimistic, and zero variance.

5.1. *Recapitulation of Parameter Alternatives.* We have evaluated the following alternatives:

(1) *Demand*—Eight alternatives. Two levels of demand, four conditions of error (counting zero error or certainty).

(2) *Interest Rates*—Three alternatives.

(3) *Import Prices*—Four alternatives. Two levels of import prices; zero penalty and positive penalty.

Thus in total the optimality of a process has been evaluated over 8 x 3 x 4 or 96 combinations of alternatives. Since a process can conceivably have its minimum cost of each stage of the process in any one of 20 time periods[7] and the number of separate stages evaluated are 58 (there are 8 single-stage processes, 15 two-stage processes, 4 three-stage processes, and 2 four-stage processes), we must evaluate 96 x 58 x 20 possibilities = 113,360. This is a staggering job even for a very large capacity high speed computer, such as Michigan State University's CDC 3600 which we employed. Fortunately the mathematical analysis which underlies our evaluation is able to shortcut many steps, and preliminary computer evaluation revealed the effects of varying conditions, so that we did not have to compute each possible set of all parameter alternatives for each of the process alternatives, in order to locate a much smaller group of process alternatives in which the optimal process was contained. As a result, the selection of the optimal process could be made on approximately three hours of CDC 3600 operation.

The purpose of using these parameter conditions is to determine how sensitive the choice of the optimal process is to variations in the values of these parameters. It is almost certain that the processes will shift their relative ranking as these conditions vary, and that the optimal timing of the installation of the stages will change as the parameter alternatives change. It is hoped, however, the optimal process will not be sensitive; or alternatively we can select that set of conditions which appear most probable

---

7. In the actual programming, 9-month periods were used giving us twenty periods for a fifteen-year planning period.

to the Venezuelan authorities, and take the optimal process for that set of conditions.

By judiciously choosing values of these parameters we can cover a broad spectrum of conditions in which the actual conditions are almost certainly to be contained. We have thus done all that it is possible to do to spell out the implications of choice, and to narrow the risk of selecting a process whose staging and phasing is not optimal—i.e., of Venezuela incurring costs which it need not incur to produce flat steel products.

6. *The Length of the Planning Period*

The duration of the planning period chosen is of importance in the selection of an optimal program, since (as in Venezuela where steel requirements are virtually certain to increase with time and where economies of scale exist as in steel) a program optimal for a five-year planning horizon is highly unlikely to be optimal for a ten- or fifteen-year horizon. Planning horizons cannot, however, be extended very far into the future. First, the estimates of requirements particularly in the steel industry become highly uncertain the longer the time period; second, even moderate discount rates tend to reduce the present value of future benefits sharply as the future grows longer; third, the technology of steel is rapidly changing so that commitments to a particular technology for a long period may result in substantial waste of capital. Considering all these factors, we have chosen a 15-year planning period, starting in 1969—the first full year in which it is possible for a steel expansion program, undertaken now, to become operational.

7. *Outputs of the Model*

The computer program was designed to provide the following outputs—for each process alternative examined, that is to say for each one listed in Table II, under the 96 sets of parameter alternatives:

(a) The optimal staging and time phasing;

(b) the total discounted costs over the planning period under (a) above;

(c) ranking the processes by total discounted costs (lowest cost = 1);

(d) the total imports required each year, for each of the four steel products in dollars and tons;

(e) the total discounted value of imports for each product;

(f) the unit costs for each product each year, excluding the costs of imports;

(g) the unit capital costs per product each year;

(h) the total revenues, costs and profits each year using the two import price levels at zero cost penalty. These figures are strictly comparable to private accounting—where the opportunity rate of interest is included as a cost;

(i) the total output in tons, by product each year.

This is a very large output due to the 96 parameter alternatives, and the supplementary economic and accounting information which it is desirable to have—that is, items (d) through (i) above. The basic computer routine is of course designed to give items (a) and (b), which are the heart of the problem. It is a very complex routine and it took longer to get it operational (about six months) than it took to solve the mathematical problems involved in the formulation, analysis, and solution of the model.

7.1. *Optimal Timing*

The analysis of so much output is itself a chore. We present several of the tables which are unique to this analysis for some selected processes for selected parameter alternatives. Table V shows for some process alternatives under certain parameter conditions (identified at the end of the table), the optimal timing, and the optimal staging. The number "0" in the optimal timing column means the first period of the twenty planning periods, "1" is the second period and so forth. The maximum number of stages are as shown in Table II for the particular process. In the optimal timing column a four-stage process—for example, process No. 18—will have four digits associated with it in the optimal timing column, a three-stage process will have three digits and so forth. Process 18, for example, under the eight parameter alternatives shown has the following sets of digits.

Process 18 (Maximum 4 stages)

Parameter Alternative	Optimal Timing
1	0012
2	0012
3	0012
4	0012
5	1134
6	1134
7	88910
8	88910

The above information tells us that this four-stage process should be operational in three different time periods to obtain the minimum total cost over the planning period. For the first four parameter alternatives, it tells us specifically that stage 1 and stage 2 should be operational in the first period, i.e., stage 1 and stage 2 should be considered as one stage. As the parameter alternatives change, these periods shift, so that under conditions 7 and 8 (low demand estimate, with zero error, or with realistic variance and with import prices at 90 percent of the U.S.A. price level and zero social cost penalty) process 18 has been shifted to period 8, 9, and 10, although it still is preferable under all parameter conditions to operate the first and second stages simultaneously. It need not have worked out this way—it is possible that under some parameter alternatives process 18 would be optimally phased as a four-stage process (the maximum designed) under some as a three-stage process or two or one. It is interesting to note the phasing sensitivity of process 18 to a change of 10 percent in the import price level (zero social cost penalty). Parameter condition 5 is identical with 7 except that 7

TABLE V

Time Phasing of Selected Process Alternatives
Under Eight Parameter Conditions

Parameter Conditions	Processes	Maximum Number of Stages				Optimal Timing			
1	2	1				0			
	3	1				0			
	5	1				0			
	6	1				3			
	8	1	2			0	0		
	9	1	2			0	0		
	10	1	2			0	0		
	11	1	2			0	0		
	17	1	2			0	1		
	18	1	2	3	4	0	0	1	2
	19	1	2	3		0	1	2	
	20	1	2	3		0	0	0	
	21	1	2			0	0		
2	2	1				0			
	3	1				0			
	5	1				0			
	6	1				3			
	8	1	2			0	0		
	9	1	2			0	0		
	10	1	2			0	0		
	11	1	2			0	0		
	17	1	2			0	1		
	18	1	2	3	4	0	0	1	2
	19	1	2	3		0	1	2	
	20	1	2	3		0	0	0	
	21	1	2			0	0		
3	2	1				0			
	3	1				0			
	5	1				2			
	6	1				7			

TABLE V *(Cont.)*

Parameter Conditions	Processes	Maximum Number of Stages				Optimal Timing			
	8	1	2			0	0		
	9	1	2			0	0		
	10	1	2			0	0		
	11	1	2			3	3		
	17	1	2			0	1		
	18	1	2	3	4	0	0	1	2
	19	1	2	3		0	1	2	
	20	1	2	3		3	3	3	
	21	1	2			3	3		
4	2	1				0			
	3	1				0			
	5	1				2			
	6	1				7			
	8	1	2			0	0		
	9	1	2			0	0		
	10	1	2			0	0		
	11	1	2			3	3		
	17	1	2			0	1		
	18	1	2	3	4	0	0	1	2
	19	1	2	3		0	1	2	
	20	1	2	3		3	3	3	
	21	1	2			3	3		
5	2	1				0			
	3	1				0			
	5	1				6			
	6	1				20			
	8	1	2			0	0		
	9	1	2			0	0		
	10	1	2			0	0		
	11	1	2			7	7		
	17	1	2			0	3		
	18	1	2	3	4	1	1	3	4

TABLE V (Cont.)

Parameter Conditions	Processes	Maximum Number of Stages				Optimal Timing			
	19	1	2	3		0	3	4	
	20	1	2	3		7	7	7	
	21	1	2			7	7		
6	2	1				0			
	3	1				0			
	5	1				6			
	6	1				20			
	8	1	2			0	0		
	9	1	2			0	0		
	10	1	2			0	0		
	11	1	2			7	7		
	17	1	2			0	3		
	18	1	2	3	4	1	1	3	4
	19	1	2	3		0	3	4	
	20	1	2	3		7	7	7	
	21	1	2			7	7		
7	2	1				1			
	3	1				1			
	5	1				20			
	6	1				20			
	8	1	2			1	1		
	9	1	2			1	1		
	10	1	2			6	6		
	11	1	1			20			
	17	1	2			7	9		
	18	1	2	3	4	8	8	9	10
	19	1	2	3		7	9	10	
	20	1	2	3		20			
	21	1	2			20			
8	2	1				1			
	3	1				1			
	5	1				20			

TABLE V *(Cont.)*

Parameter Conditions	Processes	Maximum Number of Stages				Optimal Timing			
	6	1				20			
	8	1	2			1	1		
	9	1	2			1	1		
	10	1	2			6	6		
	11	1	2			20			
	17	1	2			7	9		
	18	1	2	3	4	8	8	9	10
	19	1	2	3		7	9	10	
	20	1	2	3		20			
	21	1	2			20			

Notes: Optimal Timing:
  0 = 1st period = 1969

The periods are *nine-month periods.*

Alternatives: All alternatives are at 9% interest and 6% depreciation, and zero social cost penalty.
  1 — Best Estimate Demand, U.S.A. import prices, no error in demand.
  2 — Best Estimate Demand, realistic variance, U.S.A. import prices.
  3 — Best Estimate Demand, 90% U.S.A. import prices, no error in demand.
  4 — Best Estimate Demand, realistic variance, 90% U.S.A. import prices.
  5 — Low Estimate Demand, U.S.A. import prices, no error in demand.
  6 — Low Estimate Demand, realistic variance, U.S.A. import prices.
  7 — Low Estimate Demand, 90% U.S.A. import prices, no error in demand.
  8 — Low Estimate Demand, realistic variance, 90% U.S.A. import prices.

assumes 10 percent lower import prices than 5; so also for condition 6 and 8. The optimal timing of conditions 5 and 6 for process 18 is 1,1,3,4; for 7 and 8 it is 8,8,9,10. When the import price is lowered by 10 percent, the optimal phasing of process 18 is postponed 7 periods (63 months) for the first two stages, and 6 periods (54 months) for stages 3 and 4. This kind of result which is quite usual (if one examines all the 96 parameter conditions for all the processes) is startling at first to most engineers and especially economists who are accustomed to think of an optimal process as a technological entity without time dates and stages; of "economies of scale," "long run," cost curves, etc.; and who have grown used to comparing all processes as if they all should be compared from the same time date or other arbitrary phasing rule of convenience.

Before leaving Table V it should be noted that any process whose optimal timing is given the number 20 (i.e., the first stage is 20) will only have one number 20 no matter what the number of stages are. Since we start from 0 as the first period the number 20 is outside the planning period (20 periods), i.e., it is the twenty-first period. This means that it is cheaper to import over the total planning period than to have that process operational even at optimal timing during the planning period. One can see from Table VI that many processes which are superior to imports under optimal phasing given the "best" estimate demand, are excluded from consideration under low estimate demand. Thus process 6, the fully continuous hot strip mill with tandem cold mills, which is the largest capacity process considered as a single-stage process (such as we build in the U.S.A., but with almost twice the capacity as the one considered in this analysis), will achieve its lowest total costs within the planning period at periods 3, or 7, depending upon parameter conditions 1 through 4. However, under conditions 5 through 8, it is eliminated. Under conditions 7 and 8, it is joined by four more of the processes as shown in Table VI. These results simply underscore the necessity of breaking away from thinking of expansion as a problem of choosing a technical process and its capacity on some single set of parameter conditions.

7.2. *The Comparison of the Minimum Cost Phasing for the Alternatives Examined*

Having Table V of course means that we now know the optimal timings for each alternative. To do this the algorithm, also of necessity, computed the total discounted costs of each alternative for which it found the optimal phasing.

Table IV shows the ranking of the process alternatives according to the set of parameter conditions which we believe contain the essential conditions. They do not show all the combinations of the 96 parameter alternatives. But the processes shown as optimal (rank 1) are still optimal under all the other conditions though of course the phasing changes. One process, nonoptimal under the conditions shown, does become optimal under some of the conditions not included in this summary—though included in the full computer results. We discuss this process at a later point. In Table VI, the cost of the optimal process is taken as 1.00 and the costs of all the other processes are expressed as a relative of the optimal process, (accurate to only two decimal places). Thus one can see that the spread in total costs (costs

TABLE VI

Rank of Process in Terms of Cost Index

(Present Value Cost Over the 15-Year Planning Period, 1969-1983)
Least Cost Process Takes Rank 1, with Index 1.00

PARAMETER ALTERNATIVES	II		IV		VI		VIII	
Rank	Processes	Index	Processes	Index	Processes	Index	Processes	Index
1	19, 18	1.00	19, 18	1.00	19, 18	1.00	19, 18	1.00
2	17	1.02	17	1.02	17	1.04	17	1.02
3	5, 11, 20, 21	1.14	3	1.12	3	1.07	3	1.03
4	3, 4, 9, 10	1.15	4, 5, 9, 10	1.13	9	1.08	9	1.04
5	6	1.16	11, 20, 21	1.14	2	1.10	2	1.05
6	2, 8	1.20	6	1.15	8	1.11	8	1.06
7	1	1.23	2, 8	1.26	4	1.12	4, 10	1.07
8	7	1.24	1	1.18	10	1.13	1	1.08
9	22, 23, 24		7	1.19	1	1.14	7	1.09
10	14, 15	1.30	12, 13, 14, 15, 16, 22, 23, 24, 25, 26, 27	1.21	7	1.15	5, 6, 11, 13, 13, 14, 15, 16, 20, 21, 22, 23, 24, 25, 26, 27	1.10
11	16, 25, 26	1.31			5, 11, 20, 21	1.21		
12	12, 13, 27	1.32			22, 23, 24	1.24		
13					14	1.25		
14					6, 12, 13, 15, 16, 25, 26, 27	1.26		

NOTE: Each process cost is determined at the optimal phasing over the planning period.

of production plus costs of necessary imports discounted) under parameter alternative II (9 percent interest rate, 6 percent depreciation, best estimate demand, realistic variance, U.S.A. export prices and zero penalty for imports) is such that the worst process is 32 percent more costly than the best. Under parameter alternative 8, where the low import prices and low demands are used (somewhat lower than the engineering consultants' estimates as Chart 3 reveals), the spread is 10 percent.

Table VII shows the costs of the processes in millions of B's (discounted at 9 percent). It is apparent that process 19 is only insignificantly better than 18 (between 1 and 3 million B's) in total costs. However, one can see that the difference in costs quickly becomes substantial beyond the first rank. Thus process 17, the second best, is between 55 million and 120 million B's more costly than 19, depending upon the parameter conditions. Process 5, the third-ranked process, is almost 700 million B's more costly than 19 (parameter alternative II). As can be seen, process 5, which is ranked third under parameter alternative II, changes its position drastically when low demand is used and/or low import prices, and shares the last ranking with 15 other processes under parameter alternative VIII.

TABLE VII
Rank of Process in Terms of Cost
(Present Value Costs Over the 15-Year Planning Period, 1969-1983)
Least Cost Process Takes Rank 1

PARAMETER ALTERNATIVES	II		IV		VI		VIII	
Rank / Processes		Cost (Millions of B's)	Processes	Cost (Millions of B's)	Processes	Cost (Millions of B's)	Processes	Cost (Millions of B's)
1	19, 18	5039, 5040	19, 18	4965, 4967	19, 18	2759, 2762	19, 18	2852, 2853
2	17	5159	17	5086	17	2870	17	2907
3	5, 11, 20, 21	5724, 5751, 5750, 5751	3	5575	3	2960	3	2943
4	3, 4, 9, 10	5805, 5770, 5817, 5789	4, 5, 9, 10	5587, 5634, 5587, 5607	9	2973	9	2954

PARAMETER ALTERNATIVES		II		IV		VI		VIII
		Cost (Millions		Cost (Millions		Cost (Millions		Cost (Millions
Rank	Processes	of B's)	Processes	of B's)	Processes	of B's)	Processes	of B's)
5	6	5860	11, 20, 21	5655, 5654, 5655	2	3042	2	3005
6	2, 8	6032, 6044	6	5712	8	3053	8	3016
7	1	6202	2, 8	5740, 5751	4	3090	4, 10	3041, 3053
8	7	6233	1	5876	10	3109	1	3085
9	22, 23, 24	6341, 6366, 6353	7	5906	1	3145	7	3106
10	14, 15	6549, 6563	12, 13, 14, 15, 16, 22, 23, 24, 25, 26, 27	6006	7	3174	5, 6, 11, 12, 13, 14, 15, 16, 20, 21, 22, 23, 26, 25, 26, 27	3128
11	16, 25, 26	6594, 6594, 6577			5, 11, 20, 21	3328, 3344, 3343, 3304		
12	12, 13, 27	6674, 6674, 6669			22, 23, 24	3415, 3425, 3419		
13					14	3435		
14					6, 12, 13, 15, 16, 25, 26, 27	3475		

NOTE: Each process cost is determined at its optimal phasing over the planning period. A Bolivar (B) was approximately 22¢ at the time of the study.

Thus the analysis has identified *the* optimal process—process 19. As it turns out it is always an optimal process under the full range of conditions (the 96 parameter alternatives) though for some of these conditions other processes are just as good. Its total expected costs change, as also its timing, depending upon the parameter conditions used. However, the important point is that the solution happens to be stable—i.e., process 19 is always included in the optimal set (sometimes unique).

A point of considerable general significance is that the same technological process with identical equipment and capacity shows great differences in minimum total costs depending upon how it is staged.

(a) Process 5, 11, 17, 18, 19, 20, and 21, are in fact, when they are fully staged, identical technical processes, and all are fully integrated. They differ in the ways in which they are staged. And for each staging the optimal phasing has been determined, so that for each process, we compare only the minimum total costs of the process (discounted) over the entire planning period. Process 5 is the single-stage version of all the other processes, fully integrated. All the other processes when their staging is complete, are identical with 5 in all respects.

It can be seen that the different stagings each have some advantages and some disadvantages. Adding cold mills as the first stages meets the requirements of Venezuela for the most expensive products, i.e., tinplate and cold rolled sheets including galvanized sheets. It does not produce plates, the demand for which is low in the early periods and hot rolled sheets. Since hot mills are not installed, no pressure is placed on the 1100 m.m. mill, and hence no pressure is placed on prior stages, i.e., steel, iron, etc. Investment is low in this kind of staging; but metallic input costs are higher since hot rolled coils must be imported. Thus all the different staging possibilities have different sorts of advantages and disadvantages, and it is not possible a priori to tell which is best. As the following compilation from Table VII, parameter alternative II, and VIII shows, the differences in total cost over the planning period (costs of production plus costs of imports) are very large:

Minimum Costs of Identical Technical Process Staged Differently

Process	II Cost Millions of B's	VIII Cost Millions of B's
5	5724	3128
11	5751	3128

17	5159	2907
18	5040	2853
19	5039	2852
20	5750	3128
21	5751	3128

Under best estimate demand (realistic error) and U.S.A. import prices, the spread is as we have noted over 700 million B's (discounted to present value at 9 percent) in the identical plant, differently staged. Even in relatively minor differences in staging such as between 17 and 19, the difference is 120 million B's. Again it is important to note that this is the difference between the minimum total cost of production plus costs of necessary imports with each of the processes. This is the expected cost to the total economy of Venezuela to meet its total steel requirements over the planning period. If we ignored the cost of imports as a private entrepreneur would—the differences in the total costs of production would of course be less.

7.3. *Unstable Phasing*

We have found that process 19 is the optimal process for all 96 conditions. A question remains, however, as to its phasing stability. We found that the optimal process shows phasing stability with respect to interest rate, error, import prices, and social costs penalty under best estimate demand. It shifts to later periods with different combinations of low demand and import prices, as shown in the following compilation:

Optimal Phasing of Process 19

Best Estimate Demand—Both Import Price Levels

Stage	Time (Nearest Year)
1	1969
2	1970
3	1971

Low Demand—U.S.A. Import Prices

Stage	Time (Nearest Year)
1	1969
2	1972
3	1973

Low Demand—Low Import Prices

Stage	Time (Nearest Year)
1	1975
2	1977
3	1978

As is evident, a great deal depends upon which set of estimates of demand and import prices one wishes to rely upon in determining the time of expansion. A priori there is no way of knowing whether the phasing will be stable—nor whether a particular process will always be an optimal one (i.e., an optimum optimarum). As we indicated, there may be no alternatives other than to wait and get better information or to decide upon that set of conditions which one thinks most likely, or to get a decision rule which points uniquely to one set of conditions or one best program. In this case, luck is with us—for analysis of the output data reveals that process 19 is a best process, and further that even the apparent variation in optimal phasing may be shown to involve little risk. *That is, the results show conclusively that the risk of making a wrong decision is very low if Venezuela installs the first stage of process 19 by 1969 or 1970.* This conclusion requires a little explanation as it is not immediately obvious from the phasing dates shown above.

(a) The optimal phasing of process 19, shows that if best estimate demand is correct, then whether import prices are at U.S.A. levels or only 90 percent of U.S.A. levels, the first stage of process 19 should be operational during 1969. This is also the optimal timing for low demand, but with U.S.A. import prices. We feel very confident that the actual demand will certainly fall no lower than our low estimate. Thus for any demand higher than the low estimate and for any expected demand as high as the best estimate with 30 percent standard deviation, the optimal timing is 1969-1970 for stage 1 of process 19. We have therefore to deal with the case of low demand and low import prices where the evaluation shows that 1975 is the optimal timing of the first stage of process 19.

(b) It can be seen by reference to Table IV that the first stage of process 19 is in fact identical to process 3 treated as a single-stage fully integrated process whose investment is 673 million B's and which provides an annual capacity of 230,000 tons of cold rolled sheets, 173,000 tons of hot rolled sheets, 75,000 tons of plates, and 115,000 tons of tin plate. Table VII shows that process 3 under parameter alternative VIII, if it were not expanded further during the 15-year period, is only slightly inferior to process 19, in which all three stages would be installed (under parameter alternative VIII). The difference in total costs amounts to 91 million B's over the 15-year period. Reference to Table V shows that process 3 under all parameter alternatives 1 through 6 should be installed in period 0—i.e., 1969, and under 7 and 8, in period 1, i.e., 1970.

Thus if demand conditions are above the low estimate then stage 1 of 19, or to give it its other name, "process 3, single-stage," is optimally timed if installed in either 1969 or 1970. If parameter alternative 8 prevails then the optimal timing of process 3 is also period 1 or 1970.

The important point is that the critical stage of action is the *initial* stage. By installing process 3, or stage 1 of process 19, *no necessary commitment is made to expand these facilities* into process 19 in accordance with the evaluation based upon the information we have *now*. The analysis can easily be recomputed on the basis of more current data. Thus over the entire spectrum of conditions, the best action is to plan now for the installation of stage 1 of process 19 or its equivalent process 3— i.e., the fully integrated expansion indicated above. None of the other lower or higher capacity single-stage processes are better than process 3, except process 5 under conditions of U.S.A. import prices, best estimate demand, and when the interest rate is 9 percent or lower. Under all other conditions 3-8, process 3 is superior to all other single-stage processes evaluated.

(c) Though process 5 is better than process 3, under parameter alternatives which we believe to be reasonable, and more likely to prevail than most other combinations, it is still the best action to install process 3 rather than process 5. For if these conditions do in fact prevail, then process 3 is treated as the first stage of process 19, which as we have seen is process 5 staged, and where the staging results in a saving of approximately 700 million B's compared to process 5 under this parameter alternative.

7.4. *Improving Process Design*

Process 19 is the best process of all we have evaluated. Nevertheless, it is very likely that a modification of its capacity will result in an even more economical process. This is evident if one examines the time phasing of the three stages of process 19 under the various parameter alternatives. Thus under parameter alternative II, which we believe most likely, the first two stages are only one period apart; and under VIII, they are only two periods apart—though the timing of all the stages is delayed by eight periods. The second stage of process 19 calls for doubling the tinplate capacity and increasing the cold rolled sheet capacity by almost 80 percent. Given the parameter conditions, the introduction of the second stage 1 to 3 periods later than the first stage is indeed the optimal timing. However, the possibility of redesigning the second stage or the first stage to more closely conform to the expected demand is an obvious one to explore. It seems reasonable that either the tinplate capacity of the first stage might increase, or the capacity of the second stage be lowered. However, one must avoid assuming that such changes will necessarily result in lower total costs over the planning period. Any alteration which design engineers can suggest in the equipment, capacity, etc., can with our procedure be evaluated so long as the capital and operating costs are given.

7.5.   *Integration vs. Nonintegration*

A fully integrated expansion of flat products for Venezuela is superior to partial integration or nonintegration for optimal processes.

(a) Fully integrated production requires the expansion of steel and iron making capacity. The investment in these additional facilities to meet the metallic inputs required to balance the capacity of the flat products processes is of course very heavy. For the optimal process it adds an estimated 573 million B's to investment. We have assumed that the steel process that will be adopted will be the L-D furnace operating on a 70 percent hot iron charge and 30 percent scrap. These assumptions concerning the steel process are intended only as an approximation in order to evaluate the merits of fully integrated production versus imports of metallic inputs, i.e., slabs, hot rolled coils, etc. We believe that both the operating costs and the capital costs used are conservative. That is to say, evaluation of a wide variety of steel and iron making processes, furnace sizes, etc., will reveal processes more economical than we have assumed.

(b) Table VIII shows that full integration is substantially superior to partial integration under parameter alternatives II and VIII.

8.   *Concluding Remarks*

8.1.   *Sequential Decision Making*

Though the heart of the expansion problem lies in the correct solution of the staging and phasing of the various kinds of capacities, it would be misleading to suppose that a solution once given must be followed literally. This cannot, of course, be the case since as time progresses more information will be received, which may necessitate alteration of the "optimal" expansion program as determined *now* on *current information*. For example, estimates of future demand should constantly be revised each year to determine whether the actual results are consistent with the projected demand estimates. For even though these are made on a probabilistic basis with assumed standard deviations, it is possible that very significant changes can occur—enough to warrant revising the demand projections and re-evaluating to see whether the changes affect the staging and timing as initially formulated.

TABLE VIII

Effect of Integration on Identical Technological Processes Identically Staged for Parameter Alternatives II and VIII in Millions of B's over the Total Planning Period

									Difference Integrated–Slabs Imported	
	Fully Integrated				Slabs Imported					
Process	Invest-ment	Total Costs II	VIII	Process	Invest-ment	Total Costs II	VIII	Invest-ment	Total Costs II	VIII
19	1288	5039	2852	24	715	6353	3128	573	(1314)	(276)
18	1302	5040	2853	23	729	6366	3128	573	(1326)	(275)
17	1271	5159	2907	22	699	6341	3128	373	(1182)	(221)
11	1302	5751	3128	16	729	6594	3128	573	(843)	0
20	1301	5750	3128	25	728	6594	3128	573	(844)	0
21	1302	5751	3128	26	699	6577	3128	603	(826)	0
9	687	5817	2954	14	358	6549	3128	329	(732)	(174)
10	906	5789	3053	15	513	6563	3128	393	(774)	(75)
8	659	6044	3016	13	363	6674	3128	296	(630)	(112)

The above consideration points to the key importance of the *first staging and phasing* of the optimal process being correct. For it is the first choice in steel expansion which imposes the most severe constraints upon future action. With respect to making a decision *now* as to what to do in the future, the only choices are to rely upon *current* information (all that there is), or to *postpone a decision* and wait for more information. In this analysis of course we use current information and determine the optimal solution *on that information*.

It is, of course, true that the first installation, on the basis of five-year hindsight, (say in 1970) might be incorrect. For example, demand might have increased so rapidly between 1965 and 1970, that over the planning period process 6, a fully continuous hot mill with tandem cold mills, was optimal (on the information available in 1970) with some different staging and phasing than initially determined. On the new information, then, the problem becomes (in 1970) one of evaluating the various alternatives given the existence of the existing facilities. There is no way of avoiding such risks of making initial errors. But we believe we have done all that is possible to minimize this risk, through a method of analysis capable of examining a large number of alternatives under a large number of conditions very close to full realism, and selecting an optimum-optimorum.

8.2. *Choice of the Optimality Criterion*

Though we chose the criterion of minimizing total expected cost, it is not necessary to choose such a criterion. Any other criterion could be chosen so long as a method of computing this was available, and these criteria would vary with expected output and be a function of the alternative processes. Even weighted measures combining accounting cost, social cost, foreign exchange employment, etc., could be an optimality criterion if they met the above two conditions.

8.3. *Use of the Single-Sector Model in Overall Economic Planning*

As we have noted in Chapter I, the single-sector optimal solution could and probably would be suboptimal under total or "n" sector expansion planning. As the latter problem is not solved, we believe it is useful to solve the single-sector problem optimally. However if each of the n sectors were solved, each one by a single-sector analysis, useful information would be available for sensible solutions probably moving in the direction of an optimal n sector simultaneous solution (i.e., with all relevant interactions considered.) These n single-sector optimal solutions could be aggregated to show the additional investment, foreign exchange, output, and employment resulting from the sector expansion plans. Doubtlessly they would exceed some of the existing constraints in some of the years on these overall factors. In this case, some of the sector expansion plans would have to be cut back or postponed, in order that the aggregate requirements (in terms of available capital, manpower and foreign exchange if these are the limiting factors) do not exceed the constraints. One useful result from the single-sector analyses would be to show the additional costs of selecting alternative programs, or of postponing programs for specified time periods. Presumably one would wish to cut back or postpone some sub-set of the n sectors in such a way that the additional cost of these postponements (or alternate selections) would be a minimum, while the aggregate of the requirements of additional capital, foreign exchange, and manpower are as close to the available quantities of these (the constraint levels) as possible without exceeding them. This is a formidable problem, which we have not yet solved. It is of course another way of approaching the n-sector problem, which may have some promise.

Appendix I

A STOCHASTIC, MULTISTAGE, MULTIPRODUCT INVESTMENT MODEL*

V. P. SREEDHARAN† AND H. H. WEIN‡

Abstract. This paper presents a model for an n-stage multiproduct investment program. The problem of finding an "optimal" investment program is of great interest in industry.[1] Given a probabilistic estimate of future product(s) demand, we seek an optimum within a set of alternatives open to us. By the optimum we mean the minimum-minimorum of the total expected costs. The minimal cost and precise timing of the n stages are obtained by solving a set of functional equations using a combination of the recursive technique of dynamic programming and numerical methods.

1. Introduction. In this paper we discuss the formulation, analysis and solution of a mathematical model intended for use in selecting among alternative multistage investment programs. Such selection problems frequently confront both state planning agencies and private companies. The chosen program is to be that which is least costly (or most profitable) in the "present worth" sense.

The investments are to be used to provide capacity to meet future demands for one or more products of a given class. There may be significant penalties for either an excess or a deficit of capacity, the latter being met by "imports." Demands are regarded as "known" only in the form of probability distributions, so that it is really the expected value of discounted cost which is to be minimized.

The alternative programs will in general differ in their individual product capacities, investment requirements and operating costs. Some of them may involve the production of only a subset of the class of products being considered. Each alternative, however, must be capable of being "staged" over time. That is, facilities and capacity can be built up gradually (the model assumes discrete steps). All the "stages" of an alternative are required to be compatible; i.e., nonoperational combinations of stages are excluded.

The sequential stages of each alternative may be thought of as the sequential expansion of a multiproduct facility. In comparing alternatives

* Received by the editors June 23, 1965, and in revised form August 26, 1966.

† Department of Mathematics, Michigan State University, East Lansing, Michigan.

‡ Department of Management, Graduate School of Business Administration, Michigan State University, East Lansing, Michigan.

[1] The authors wish to thank the Corporacion Venezolana De Guayana for support of this research and to acknowledge the assistance of Dr. Pedro Maal in the economic formulation of this problem. We are also indebted to the referee for his useful comments.

one should associate, to each, that precise timing of its stages (i.e., the times when the stages should become operational) which minimizes the mean discounted cost. Thus the "best" alternative is selected as a minimum-minimorum.

Our effort is therefore focussed on the problem of determining the optimal time-phasing, for some one alternative which is completely specified *except* for this phasing. A mathematical model for this problem is developed in §2. Section 3 describes a solution method using the recursive technique of dynamic programming.

The solution has been applied to the selection of the optimal phasing over a fifteen-year planning period for twenty-seven different process alternatives for producing flat steel products (four in number). This was done for a South American country in which the steel facilities are state owned. The minimum-minimorum was determined under a variety of alternative assumptions on parameters such as interest rate, import prices, varying growth rates and assumed errors in these.

As it turned out the processes showed significant phasing sensitivity depending upon parameter values (eight sets of parameter values were tested). But under the four parameter alternatives considered most likely to prevail the minimum-minimorum was stable. Because of the lengthiness of the descriptive empirical material and results we do not include them in this paper. They are intended to be published elsewhere.

2. Formulation of model. The "present" will as usual be denoted by $t = 0$. We use the notation

$$T = \text{planning horizon},$$

$$n = \text{number of stages}.$$

The variables of our minimization problem are denoted by

(1) $$0 \leq t_1 \leq t_2 \leq \cdots \leq t_n \leq T,$$

where t_i is the time at which the ith stage begins. Note that the possible equalities in (1) admit simultaneous initiation of several stages.

For compactness, we set $\mathbf{t}_n = (t_1, \cdots, t_n)$ and let $\Delta(n, T)$ denote that portion of $\mathbf{t}_n$-space defined by (1). The minimization problem consists of determining

(2) $$f(n, T) = \min \{F^{(n)}(\mathbf{t}_n ; T) \mid \mathbf{t}_n \in \Delta(n, T)\},$$

and finding $\mathbf{t}_n^*$ at which the minimum is attained. We proceed to describe the explicit form of the function $F^{(n)}$.

The alternative whose timing is under study involves the quantities

K_i = amount of capital invested at the beginning of the ith stage,

i.e., at t_i .

Note that some of the K_i may be zero. With the notations

$$\alpha = \text{discounting rate,}$$

$$\beta = \text{salvage rate,}$$

we see that at time T the worth of the facilities introduced for the ith stage is $K_i \exp\{-\beta(T - t_i)\}$, which discounted back to t_i becomes

$$K_i \exp\{-(\beta + \alpha)(T - t_i)\}.$$

Hence effective net capital expended at t_i is

$$K_i - K_i \exp\{-(\beta + \alpha)(T - t_i)\},$$

whose contribution to the present worth function $F^{(n)}(\mathbf{t}_n ; T)$ is

$$K_i \exp(-\alpha t_i) - K_i \exp\{-(\beta + \alpha)T + \beta t_i\}.$$

Thus one summand of $F^{(n)}(\mathbf{t}_n ; T)$ is

(3) $$\sum_{i=1}^{n} K_i[\exp(-\alpha t_i) - \exp\{-(\beta + \alpha)T + \beta t_i\}].$$

The different products will be indexed $j = 1, \cdots, p$, where p denotes the total number of products. The investment policy alternative involves certain quantities

ρ_{ij} = capacity for jth product in ith stage.

The existence of the facilities involves certain fixed costs

d_{ij} = unit (of capacity) cost associated with jth product in ith stage,

while the operation of the facilities brings in variable costs

c_{ij} = unit (of output) cost for jth product in ith stage.

The demand functions

$d_j(t)$ = demand rate for jth product at time t

are assumed to be exogenous. Actual output rate is given by

(4) $$r_{ij}(t) = \min(\rho_{ij}, d_j(t)), \qquad\qquad t \in [t_i, t_{i+1}],$$

with $t_{n+1} = T$. In other words, there is no "stockpiling." Note that some ρ_{ij} may be zero; in fact, we might for some j have *all* $\rho_{ij} = 0$.

The aforementioned costs lead to another summand of $F^{(n)}(t_n \; ; \; T)$, namely,

$$(5) \qquad E\left[\sum_{i=1}^{n} \sum_{j=1}^{p} \int_{t_i}^{t_{i+1}} \{ c_{ij} \, r_{ij}(t) + d_{ij} \, \rho_{ij} \} \exp\,(-\alpha t) \, dt \right],$$

where the expectation operator E is required because the integrands r_{ij} involve the stochastic demand functions d_j.

The terms $d_{ij}\rho_{ij}$ in (5) impose a penalty for *excess* capacity. The remaining summand of $F^{(n)}$ expresses the cost of the "imports" (for a government actual imports, and for a private firm items purchased but not necessarily from abroad) required to compensate for *inadequate* capacity. Let

$$M_j = \text{delivered "import" unit price of } j\text{th product.}$$

The total discounted expenditure for imports is then given by

$$\sum_{j=1}^{p} M_j \int_{0}^{t_1} d_j(t) \exp\,(-\alpha t) \, dt$$

$$+ \sum_{i=1}^{n} \sum_{j=1}^{p} M_j \int_{t_i}^{t_{i+1}} [d_j(t) - r_{ij}(t)] \exp\,(-\alpha t) \, dt.$$

For underdeveloped countries, however, imports may be viewed as having "extra costs," dictated by the amount of foreign exchange available, national aspirations, etc. These "social costs" of imports are generally viewed as rising nonlinearly with the size of the import. We incorporate this by introducing a square term. The coefficients μ and λ of the penalty function (as well as the import prices M_j) could be treated as time-varying without any conceptual difficulties, but this would require unattainably complete knowledge of the future economy in the large, and much more cumbersome computations. Thus the final term of $F^{(n)}(t_n \; ; \; T)$ reads

$$E\left\{ \sum_{j=1}^{p} M_j \left[\int_{0}^{t_1} \{ \mu \, d_j(t) + \lambda \, d_j^2(t) \} \exp\,(-\alpha t) \, dt \right.\right.$$

$$(6) \qquad + \sum_{i=1}^{n} \int_{t_i}^{t_{i+1}} \{ \mu(d_j(t) - r_{ij}(t))$$

$$\left.\left. + \lambda(d_j(t) - r_{ij}(t))^2 \} \exp\,(-\alpha t) \, dt \right] \right\}.$$

To summarize, the minimization problem in (2) takes the explicit form

$$f(n, T) = \min \{ F^{(n)}(t_n \; ; \; T) \mid t_n \in \Delta(n, T) \}$$

$$= \min_{\mathbf{t}_n \in \Delta(n,T)} \left\{ \sum_{i=1}^{n} K_i[\exp(-\alpha t_i) - \exp\{-(\beta + \alpha)T + \beta t_i\}] \right.$$

$$(7) \qquad + E\left(\sum_{j=1}^{p} \left[M_j \int_0^{t_1} \{\mu d_j(t) + \lambda d_j^2(t)\} \exp(-\alpha t) \, dt \right.\right.$$

$$+ \sum_{i=1}^{n} \int_{t_i}^{t_{i+1}} \{c_{ij} r_{ij}(t) + d_{ij} \rho_{ij}$$

$$\left.\left.\left. + M_j[\mu(d_j(t) - r_{ij}(t)) + \lambda(d_j(t) - r_{ij}(t))^2]\} \exp(-\alpha t) \, dt \right] \right) \right\}.$$

3. Analysis. One now recognizes the possibility of applying some recursive technique such as that in Bellman [1]. With this purpose in mind, and regarding T as fixed, we define $G^{(n)}$ to be that part of $F^{(n)}$ arising from the interval $[0, t_n)$. Thus, for $0 \leq t_n \leq T$ and $\mathbf{t}_{n-1} \in \Delta(n-1, t_n)$, let

$$G^{(n)}(\mathbf{t}_{n-1}; t_n) = \sum_{i=1}^{n-1} K_i\{\exp(-\alpha t_i) - \exp(-(\beta + \alpha)T + \beta t_i)\}$$

$$+ E\left(\sum_{j=1}^{p} \left[\sum_{i=1}^{n-1} \int_{t_i}^{t_{i+1}} \{c_{ij} r_{ij}(t) + d_{ij} \rho_{ij} \right.\right.$$

$$(8) \quad + M_j[\mu(d_j(t) - r_{ij}(t)) + \lambda(d_j(t) - r_{ij}(t))^2]\} \exp(-\alpha t) \, dt$$

$$\left.\left. + M_j \int_0^{t_1} \{\mu \, d_j(t) + \lambda \, d_j^2(t)\} \exp(-\alpha t) \, dt \right] \right),$$

and set

$$(9) \qquad g(n, \tau) = \min \{G^{(n)}(\mathbf{t}_{n-1}; \tau) \mid \mathbf{t}_{n-1} \in \Delta(n-1, \tau)\}.$$

It follows that

$$f(n, T) = \min_{0 \leq t \leq T} \left\{ g(n, t) + K_n[\exp(-\alpha t) - \exp(-(\beta + \alpha)T + \beta t)] \right.$$

$$(10) \qquad + E\left[\sum_{j=1}^{p} \int_t^{T} \{c_{nj} r_{nj}(s) + d_{nj} \rho_{nj} \right.$$

$$+ M_j[\mu(d_j(s) - r_{nj}(s)) + \lambda(d_j(s) - r_{nj}(s))^2]\}$$

$$\left.\left. \cdot \exp(-\alpha s) \, ds \right] \right\}.$$

Thus the evaluation of $f(n, T)$ is reduced to a one-dimensional minimization problem—*if* we have an efficient method for calculating the values of $g(n, \tau)$. Such a method, however, can be arrived at by observing that the function $G^{(n)}$ obeys the recursion

$$G^{(n)}(\mathbf{t}_{n-1}\,;\,t_n) = G^{(n-1)}(\mathbf{t}_{n-2}\,;\,t_{n-1})$$

$$+ K_{n-1}\{\exp(-\alpha t_{n-1}) - \exp(-(\beta + \alpha)T + \beta t_{n-1})\}$$

$$(11) \qquad + E\left[\sum_{j=1}^{p}\int_{t_{n-1}}^{t_n}\{c_{n-1,j}r_{n-1,j}(t) + d_{n-1,j}\rho_{n-1,j}\right.$$

$$+ M_j[\mu(d_j(t) - r_{n-1,j}(t))$$

$$\left. + \lambda(d_j(t) - r_{n-1,j}(t))^2]\}\exp(-\alpha t)dt\right]$$

This in turn gives us the functional equation

$$g(n,\tau) = \min_{0 \le t \le \tau}\left\{g(n-1,t)\right.$$

$$+ K_{n-1}[\exp(-\alpha t) - \exp(-(\beta + \alpha)T + \beta t)]$$

$$(12) \qquad + E\left[\sum_{j=1}^{p}\int_{t}^{\tau}\{c_{n-1,j}r_{n-1,j}(s) + d_{n-1,j}\rho_{n-1,j}\right.$$

$$+ M_j[\mu(d_j(s) - r_{n-1,j}(s))$$

$$\left.\left. + \lambda(d_j(s) - r_{n-1,j}(s))^2]\}\exp(-\alpha s)\,ds\right]\right\}$$

for $n > 1$. The "boundary condition" corresponding to $n = 1$ is

$$(13) \quad g(1,\tau) = E\left[\sum_{j=1}^{p}M_j\int_{0}^{\tau}\{\mu d_j(t) + \lambda d_j^2(t)\}\exp(-\alpha t)\,dt\right].$$

Thus the calculation of $f(n,T)$ can be carried out as a sequence of one-dimensional minimizations.

Further progress requires specifying the functional forms of the temporal and stochastic variations of the demands d_j. For initial simplicity, we assume positive constant growth rates b_j, which are themselves random variables. The more realistic nonconstant case is considered subsequently. Thus

$$(14) \qquad\qquad d_j(t) = d_j(t, b_j) = a_j \exp(b_j t), \qquad\qquad a_j, b_j > 0.$$

This analytic form allows us to define $t_{ij}(b_j)$ uniquely by the specification

$$d_j(t_{ij}(b_j), b_j) = \rho_{ij},$$

which implies that

$$(15) \qquad\qquad t_{ij}(b_j) = b_j^{-1}\log(\rho_{ij}/a_j).$$

We may abbreviate

(16) $$t_{ij}(b) = t_{ij}(b_j),$$

since it is the function t_{ij} that we are defining. It follows from (4) that

(17) $$d_j(s) - r_{ij}(s) = 0, \quad s \in [t_i, \min\{t_{ij}(b), t_{i+1}\}],$$

(18) $$r_{ij}(s) = \rho_{ij}, \quad s \in [\max\{t_i, t_{ij}(b)\}, t_{i+1}].$$

With the aid of these, one verifies that the integral occurring in (12) can be rewritten as

(19)
$$\int_t^\tau \{\cdots\} \exp(-\alpha s)\, ds = c_{ij} \int_t^{t'} c_j(s) \exp(-\alpha s)\, ds$$
$$+ d_{ij}\rho_{ij} \int_t^\tau \exp(-\alpha s)\, ds + \rho_{ij}(c_{ij} + M_j(\lambda\rho_{ij} - \mu))$$
$$\cdot \int_{t'}^\tau \exp(-\alpha s)\, ds + M_j(\mu - 2\lambda\rho_{ij}) \int_{t'}^\tau d_j(s) \exp(-\alpha s)\, ds$$
$$+ \lambda M_j \int_{t'}^\tau d_j^2(s) \exp(-\alpha s)\, ds,$$

where

(20) $$t' = t'_{ij}(b) = \max\{t, \min(t_{ij}(b), \tau)\}.$$

With the aid of (14) the integrals in (19) can of course be evaluated explicitly.

It is convenient to write[2]

(21)
$$\Lambda(x, y, \theta) = \int_x^y \exp\{(\theta - \alpha)s\}\, ds$$
$$= (\alpha - \theta)^{-1}\{\exp[(\theta - \alpha)x] - \exp[(\theta - \alpha)y]\}.$$

Then the right-hand side of (19) becomes

(22)
$$c_{ij}a_j\Lambda(t, t', b) + d_{ij}\rho_{ij}\alpha^{-1}[\exp(-\alpha t) - \exp(-\alpha\tau)]$$
$$+ \alpha^{-1}\rho_{ij}[c_{ij} + M_j(\lambda\rho_{ij} - \mu)][\exp(-\alpha t') - \exp(-\alpha\tau)]$$
$$+ M_j(\mu - 2\lambda\rho_{ij})a_j\Lambda(t', \tau, b) + \lambda M_j a_j^2 \Lambda(t', \tau, 2b).$$

The expectation operator E (cf. (12)) must be taken into account. No explicit assumption about the probability distributions of $(b_1, \cdots, b_p)$ has yet been made. For computational facility we shall assume that the distributions $P_j(b)$ of the random variables b_j are statistically independent.

---

[2] The proper indeterminate form is assumed for $\alpha = \theta$.

Hence (12) takes the explicit form

$$
g(i + 1, \tau) = \min_{0 \leq t \leq \tau} \Big\{ g(i, t) + K_i \left[\exp(-\alpha t) \right.
$$

$$
- \exp(-(\beta + \alpha)T + \beta t)] + \sum_{j=1}^{p} \Big[c_{ij} a_j \int_{-\infty}^{\infty} \Lambda(t, t', b) P_j(b) \, db
$$

$$
+ d_{ij} \rho_{ij} \alpha^{-1} \{ \exp(-\alpha t) - \exp(-\alpha \tau) \} + \alpha^{-1} \rho_{ij} \{ c_{ij}
$$

(23) $$
+ M_j(\lambda \rho_{ij} - \mu) \} \int_{-\infty}^{\infty} \{ \exp(-\alpha t') - \exp(-\alpha \tau) \} P_j(b) \, db
$$

$$
+ M_j(\mu - 2\lambda \rho_{ij}) a_j \int_{-\infty}^{\infty} \Lambda(t', \tau, b) P_j(b) \, db
$$

$$
+ \lambda M_j a_j^2 \int_{-\infty}^{\infty} \Lambda(t', \tau, 2b) P_j(b) \, db \Big] \Big\}
$$

$$
= \min_{0 \leq t \leq \tau} \varphi(i, t, \tau),
$$

say, where t' was defined in (20).

To solve the phasing problem it is necessary to keep track of the points where the minimum of $\varphi(i, t, \tau)$ occurs. Let t^* be such that

(24) $$
g(i + 1, \tau) = \varphi(i, t^*, \tau),
$$

(25) $$
t^* = t^*(i, \tau).
$$

Then in the n-stage problem, once T and n are given, $t^*(n, T)$ is the timing of the nth stage and inductively the timing of the $(n - 1)$th stage is $t^*(n - 1, t^*(n, T))$, and so on. Note that, though we explicitly defined $t^*(i, \tau)$ only for $i < n$, the obvious interpretation of $t^*(n, T)$ is used in connection with (10).

All real problems for which the preceding analysis would be useful are characterized by many investment alternatives and frequently by non-constant-growth-rates. Numerical solutions to such problems are feasible only through a digital computer, such as the CDC 3600 at Michigan State University, which was available to us. Though certain simplifications will result by assuming some reasonably simple forms for $P_j(b)$, still, the computations are much too long for a desk calculator—let alone the nonconstant-growth-rate-case.

We make the traditional but not unrealistic assumption that P_j's are normal distributions.[3] Explicitly,

(26) $$
P_j(b) = \frac{1}{\sigma_j \sqrt{2\pi}} \exp \left[-\frac{1}{2} (b - \bar{b}_j)^2 / \sigma_j^2 \right], \qquad j = 1, \cdots, p.
$$

[3] In real situations the problem of the estimation of the parameters $\bar{b}_j$ and σ_j is

To evaluate the infinite integrals in (23) we make use of the well-known Gauss-Hermite quadrature formula (see [2]) which states that

$$(27) \qquad \int_{-\infty}^{\infty} \exp\left(-x^2\right) g(x)\, dx = \sum_{k=-m}^{m} H_k g(x_k) + \epsilon_m \,,$$

where H_k are the Gauss-Hermite weights, x_k the corresponding abscissas and ϵ_m the error term. Using (26),

$$(28) \qquad \int_{-\infty}^{\infty} P_j(b) g(b)\, db = \frac{1}{\sqrt{\pi}} \int_{-\infty}^{\infty} \exp\left(-x^2\right) g(\bar{b}_j + \sqrt{2}\sigma_j x)\, dx$$

$$\approx \sum_{k=-m}^{m} w_k g(s_{jk}),$$

where

$$(29) \qquad s_{jk} = \bar{b}_j + \sqrt{2}\sigma_j x_k$$

and

$$(30) \qquad w_k = H_k / \sqrt{\pi}.$$

An appraisal of ϵ_m can be made by using a formula [2, p. 129], namely,

$$\epsilon_m = \frac{m!\sqrt{\pi}}{2^m (2m)!}\, g^{(2m)}(\eta).$$

In the present case a better estimate could be obtained by applying this formula to $\int_{-\infty}^{\infty} g_N(x) \exp\left(-x^2\right) dx$, where g_N is the truncation of g in the interval $[-N, N]$, and then making another error estimate for this truncation error using properties of $\exp\left(-x^2\right)$. Since the formula (27) is

---

of considerable importance. When there is lack of significant data to produce reasonable econometric forecasts, the possibility of estimating an optimistic, pessimistic and realistic rate of growth and then using a beta-distribution in place of the normal is not excluded. This procedure has been applied successfully in analogous situations in PERT. The attendant mathematical ramifications are evident. We have to replace the Gauss-Hermite weights and abscissas by appropriate Jacobi weights and abscissas. Of course, now the weights and abscissas themselves have to be computed by a computer routine each time since the associated Jacobi polynomials, and hence their roots, depend in a more complex way on the parameters of the beta-distribution than the Hermite polynomials on the parameters of the Gaussian distribution. A general computer program of this type would have the virtue of including such distributions as triangular and others also.

We shall present the normal case since all the remaining calculations but for the above noted initial difference are identical. Moreover, this difficulty just alluded to is somewhat routine.

exact for polynomials of degree $\leqq 2m - 1$ and since the function g is a combination of various exponentials we did not go through this procedure.

Some remarks are also in order regarding the possibility of s_{jk} becoming very negative which would be the case if we use large m. This occurs for large values of m, but in view of (17) and (18), the integrals in (19) would still be physically meaningful—provided the stochastic variations were estimated properly. The reason for this is that large negative values would occur with a low probability which would be taken into account by the quadrature formula. In our study referred to earlier, the values of σ_j and the chosen value of m were such that $s_{jk} \geqq 0$, for all j and k.

Thus, finally, (23) becomes

$$
\begin{aligned}
g(i + 1, \tau) = \min_{0 \leqq t \leqq \tau} \{ & g(i, t) \\
& + K_i[\exp(-\alpha t) - \exp(-(\beta + \alpha)T + \beta t)] \\
& + \alpha^{-1} \exp(-\alpha t) \sum_{j=1}^{p} d_{ij}\rho_{ij} - \alpha^{-1} \exp(-\alpha\tau) \sum_{j=1}^{p} \rho_{ij}\{d_{ij} \\
& + c_{ij} + M_j(\lambda\rho_{ij} - \mu)\} + \sum_{j=1}^{p} \sum_{k=-m}^{m} w_k[c_{ij}a_j\Lambda(t, t', s_{jk}) \\
& + \alpha^{-1}\rho_{ij}\{c_{ij} + M_j(\lambda\rho_{ij} - \mu)\} \exp(-\alpha t') \\
& + M_j a_j(\mu - 2\lambda\rho_{ij})\Lambda(t', \tau, s_{jk}) \\
& + \lambda M_j a_j^2 \Lambda(t', \tau, 2s_{jk})]\},
\end{aligned}
$$

(31)

where

(32) $$ t' = t'_{ij}(s_{jk}), $$

and the formula (20) is used in its computation.

We may now discretize the problem in (31) in an obvious way by choosing a fine enough grid for the planning horizon $[0, T]$. The number of subdivisions of $[0, T]$ is mostly influenced by the physical nature of the problem. That is, a very fine subdivision resulting in possible additions of facilities at quick intervals may not be realizable. In fact, the subdivisions had to be spaced six months apart in our study. Thus it seems appropriate to view the grid-size as a constraint. Equations (31), (13), (10) and other related equations are now in a form suitable for translation into an algebraic language for use on a large-scale digital computer.

In the nonconstant-growth-rate case, we assume that the demand rates for each of the p products can be approximated in the intervals $[0, T_1]$,

$[T_1, T_2]$ and $[T_2, T]$ by

$$(33) \quad d_j(t, b_j) = \begin{cases} a_j \exp{(b_j t)}, & 0 \leqq t \leqq T_1, \\ a_j \exp{[b_j\{T_1 + \theta_j(t - T_1)\}]}, & T_1 \leqq t \leqq T_2, \\ a_j \exp{[b_j\{T_1 + \theta_j(T_2 - T_1) + \bar{\theta}_j(t - T_2)\}]}, \\ & T_2 \leqq t \leqq T. \end{cases}$$

Here the demand (a_j) for each product at $t = 0$ is assumed to be known with certainty, while b_j are stochastic variables. The interpretations of (10), (12) and (13) remain unaltered, but it is necessary to replace the simple formula (15). With this in view we define

$$\begin{aligned} t_{ij}^{(1)} &= t_{ij}^{(1)}(b) = b^{-1} \log{(\rho_{ij}/a_j)}, \\ t_{ij}^{(2)} &= (\theta_j b)^{-1} \log{(\rho_{ij}/a_j)} - (1 - \theta_j)T_1/\theta_j \\ (34) \qquad &= [t_{ij}^{(1)} - (1 - \theta_j)T_1]/\theta_j, \\ t_{ij}^{(3)} &= (\bar{\theta}_j b)^{-1} \log{(\rho_{ij}/a_j)} - (1 - \theta_j)T_1/\bar{\theta}_j - (\theta_j - \bar{\theta}_j)T_2/\bar{\theta}_j \\ &= \theta_j t_{ij}^{(2)}/\bar{\theta}_j - (\theta_j/\bar{\theta}_j - 1)T_2. \end{aligned}$$

The appropriate replacement of (15) defining $t'_{ij}(b)$ is then given by the following rule:

$$(35) \quad \begin{aligned} &\text{if } t_{ij}^{(1)} \leqq T_1, \quad \text{then} \quad t_{ij}(b) = t_{ij}^{(1)}; \\ &\text{if } T_1 < t_{ij}^{(1)}, \quad t_{ij}^{(2)} \leqq T_2, \quad \text{then} \quad t_{ij}(b) = t_{ij}^{(2)}; \\ &\text{if } T_1 < t_{ij}^{(1)} \quad \text{and} \quad T_2 < t_{ij}^{(2)}, \quad t_{ij}^{(3)} \leqq T, \quad \text{then} \quad t_{ij}(b) = t_{ij}^{(3)}; \\ &\text{if } T_1 < t_{ij}^{(1)}, \quad T_2 < t_{ij}^{(2)} \quad \text{and} \quad T < t_{ij}^{(3)}, \quad \text{then} \quad t_{ij}(b) = T. \end{aligned}$$

Equations (17), (18), (19) and (20) still apply. But (19) does not simplify to (22). To get analogous expressions we put

$$\tilde{a} = a_j \exp{\{b(1 - \theta_j)T_1\}}, \qquad \tilde{b} = b\theta_j,$$

and

$$(36) \qquad \hat{a}_j = \tilde{a}_j \exp{\{(\theta_j - \bar{\theta}_j)T_2\}}, \qquad \hat{b} = b\bar{\theta}_j.$$

Let t' be defined via (35) and (20). Then the factor of c_{ij} in the first summand of (22) will be replaced by:

$$\begin{aligned} &a_j\Lambda(t, t', b) & &\text{if } 0 \leqq t \leqq t' \leqq T_1, \\ &[a_j\Lambda(t, T_1, b) + \tilde{a}_j\Lambda(T_1, t', \tilde{b})] & &\text{if } 0 \leqq t \leqq T_1 \leqq t' \leqq T_2, \\ &\tilde{a}_j\Lambda(t, t', \tilde{b}) & &\text{if } T_1 \leqq t \leqq t' \leqq T_2, \end{aligned}$$

$$[a_j\Lambda(t, T_1, b) + \tilde{a}_j\Lambda(T_1, T_2, b) + \hat{a}_j\Lambda(T_2, t', b)]$$
$$\text{if } 0 \leqq t \leqq T_1 < T_2 \leqq t',$$
$$[\tilde{a}_j\Lambda(t, T_2, \tilde{b}) + \hat{a}_j\Lambda(T_2, t', \hat{b})] \qquad \text{if } T_1 \leqq t \leqq T_2 \leqq t',$$
$$\hat{a}_j\Lambda(t, t', \hat{b}) \qquad\qquad\qquad \text{if } T_2 \leqq t \leqq t'.$$

The two middle terms in (22) remain unaltered, but the last two terms must be replaced in a fashion similar to the above. In fact, if we change t to t' and t' to τ wherever they appear in this paragraph we get the appropriate multiplier of $M_j(\mu - 2\lambda\rho_{ij})$. To obtain the multiplier of λM_j (the last summand in (22)), we need to replace b by $2b$, a_j by a_j^2, $\tilde{b}$ by $2\tilde{b}$, $\tilde{a}_j$ by $\tilde{a}_j^2$, $\hat{b}$ by $2\hat{b}$ and $\hat{a}_j$ by $\hat{a}_j^2$ in the multiplier we have just obtained for the next to the last term of (22)—of course, we do not alter the definition of t'. With these modifications, but using the same $P_j(b)$'s, we arrive at a modified version of (31), the intermediate steps and reasoning being the same as before.

This is now ready for translation into a computer program. Though our actual computer program prints much further information which is traditionally sought in accounting and economic comparisons (consistent with our definition of optimality), we have suppressed these details since they are neither mathematically interesting nor directly related to our definition of optimality. The program written in Fortran 3600 for the nonconstant-growth-rate case will be published in another paper.

The authors are considering generalizations of the present model where stochastic demands of intermediate products are permitted. The solution of this problem, we believe, would be of considerable value in the optimal investment programming of whole sets of industries related in an input-output fashion.

REFERENCES

[1] R. BELLMAN, *Dynamic Programming*, Princeton University Press, Princeton, 1957.
[2] V. I. KRYLOV, *Approximate Calculations of Integrals*, Macmillan, New York, 1962.

Appendix II

Process Alternatives for the Production of Flat Products

A. *Introduction*

1. *Processes to be Evaluated*

In this appendix, description and data on the classical methods of producing flat products is presented. These methods differ in capacity, in investment, and in total costs per ton. The selection of a particular process is usually made on the basis of market size, but as we have shown, the market estimates themselves are subject to substantial error. This, taken together with different estimates of the rate of interest, wage rates, depreciation periods, the social cost of imports and the various staging and phasing possibilities, makes it dangerous to rely upon intuition to eliminate any of the classical methods as uneconomical. This comment applies particularly to the process appropriate to the very smallest markets; i.e., the mechanized sheet and tin plate mill, and to the process used for very large markets of 1.5 million tons of flat products and more—that is, the continuous hot strip mill with tandem cold mills. We therefore include the description and cost data for these "extreme" cases. We shall ask our model to evaluate these together with the other processes which to our intuition appear to be the feasible alternatives.

We shall not evaluate in this report the various possibilities for expanding rolling mill capacity for products other than the flat products. Our analysis is confined solely to flat products assuming a source of slabs as given. Similarly we do not analyze the impact of flat production on steel and iron requirements. An optimal solution for the entire iron and steel making process from hot iron through finished products requires an extension of the method we have constructed for the flat products.

The processes which we consider for the flat products are as follows:

(a) Mechanized sheet and tin plate mills.

(b) Steckel hot strip mill and reversing cold mills.

(c) Semi-continuous hot strip mill and reversing cold mills.

(d) Semi-continuous hot strip mill and tandem cold mills.

(e) The United Engineering and Foundry proposed semi-continuous hot strip mill and tandem cold mills.

(f) The International Construction Company proposals for semi-continuous hot strip mill and reversing cold mills (Alternative 1).

(g) Continuous hot strip mill and tandem cold mills. We have not included a hot planetary mill as a possibility for the hot stages since they are of extremely low capacity, and compared to the mechanized sheet mills, they have very high maintenance costs and are subject to more frequent shutdowns.

2. *Utilization of the 1100 m.m. Mill for Flat Product Production*

In all the flat products processes we consider (other than the mechanized sheet and tin plate mills which will use sheet bars as the raw material input), the inputs are slabs. The source of slabs for all the processes, other than the continuous mill, is the Mesta 44 inch blooming-slabbing mill (1100 m.m. mill), which the existing plant has. We have checked with Mesta and there is no doubt that this mill could be modified with relatively minor expense to produce 48-inch slabs.[1] It might, with somewhat greater expense, be modified to produce a 52-inch slab—though this is not certain. Such a slab width would be appropriate for 56-inch hot mills—producing about 50-inch wide material. It is also possible to use a 66-inch hot mill, particularly if the 52-inch slab could be produced.

Substantial economies in investment result from using the existing 44-inch mill. This mill has excess capacity even if all the present finishing mills were operating at their designed capacity. The 44-inch mill is conservatively rated at 1,200,000 metric tons per year of output at 6,000 hours of operation.[2] About 625,000 tons of blooms would be required for the other mills at capacity, so that approximately half the output of the blooming-slabbing mill is available for flat products, even when the other finishing mills are operating at full capacity. As a practical matter demand for the full output for the sectional products produced by the existing plant is not likely to require this much capacity before some time in the 1970's.

3. *Classification of Flat Products and Typical Uses*

Table 1 shows the generally accepted classification of flat rolled products which are distinguished on the basis of thickness. It also shows the typical uses for each product. Depending upon the manufacturing use, the products will have to meet specifications of surface quality, ductibility, strength in two directions and shape. Not all the processes we discuss can meet all specifications for high quality flats. Auto body panels, door pillars, and brake drums, for example, will require sheets of extra deep drawing quality. Such quality cannot be achieved on a mechanized sheet mill. Galvanized sheets, for example, do not require very smooth surfaces since the zinc coating covers minor defects, so all processes can produce this quality.

---

1. "Relatively minor expense" was stated to be below $1,000,000.

2. Similar mills in the U. S. A. are rated at 1,350,000 metric tons (1,500,000 net tons) at 6,000 hours. It is also possible to exceed 6,000 hours of operation—which is 3 turns per day, 5 days per week, 50 weeks per year, and thus obtain higher capacity for the 1100 m.m. mill.

TABLE 1

Classification of Flat Products

Product	Thickness	Uses
	3 mm. and above	Heavy Machinery & Equipment
		Heavy Construction
		Shipbuilding
PLATE		Boilers
		Pressure Vessels
		Gas and Oil Pipe Lines
		Railway Freight Cars
Hot		Oil and Water Tanks
Rolled	1.2 mm. to	Light Machinery & Equipment
Material	3 mm.	Light Construction
HOT		Chassis, Wheels and
ROLLED		Brake Drums
SHEET		Drum Stock
		Pressings and Stampings
	.75 mm. to	Furniture Stock
	2.5 mm.	Electric and Gas Cookers
		Refrigerator and Washing
Cold	COLD	Machine Bodies
Rolled	ROLLED	Auto Bodies
Material	SHEET	Pressings and Stampings
	.35 mm. to	Drum Stock
	.75 mm.	Enamelling Stock
		Galvanizing Stock
	.2 mm. to	Tinplate
	.35 mm.	Blackplate
		Enamelling Stock

B. *Description of the Flat Rolling Processes*

1. *Mechanized Sheet and Tin Plate Mills*

Tin plate and sheet are each hot rolled from sheared sheet bar on separate mechanized mills, each comprising a three-high rougher and two two-high finishers arranged side by side, each with a common driving motor. A sheet bar heating furnace and two pack heating furnaces with conveyors are provided for each mill. After shearing and opening, the hot rolled tin plate is pickled and annealed and then given one, two, or three passes in the two high cold rolls prior to white annealing and tinning in hot dip tinning machines. The hot rolled sheet, after shearing, is annealed and given one pass in two high cold rolls. The tin plate and the sheet are kept entirely separate throughout the process.

2. *Steckel Hot Strip Mill and Reversing Cold Mills*

Two slab reheating furnaces are provided from which the hot slabs are fed to a reversing roughing mill 2,140 m.m. (84″) wide fitted with a turn-around for broadsiding. This mill can either roll plates or breakdowns about 20 m.m. (¾″) thick for the Steckel mill. Plates are taken off by a transfer to a plate finishing line where they are levelled and sheared to size. The breakdowns, after being given three or five passes in the reversing rougher are passed directly to the Steckel mill. After the first and subsquent passes the material being rolled in the Steckel mill is coiled on coilers situated in furnaces at either side of the mill stand. After five or seven passes the hot rolled strip passes down the runout table where it is cooled under water sprays and coiled.

A continuous pickler is provided for material to be cold rolled and also reversing cold mills, one for cold rolled sheet and one for tin plate. Tension reels are provided at each side of the cold mills and cold rolled sheet is given about three passes and tin plate about five. Tin plate, for which palm oil is used in cold rolling, is cleaned on a cleaning line. Batch coil annealing furnaces are provided, followed by two single stand temper mills, one for sheet and one for tin plate, which is given two passes for temper

3 and above. Cut-up lines for tin plate and sheet have provision for inspection and sorting of the cut sheets.

Hot finished sheet is skin passed in coil form and subsequently cut up and sorted.

3. *Semi-Continuous Hot Strip Mill and Reversing Cold Mills*

The semi-continuous hot mill employs a reversing roughing stand 2,800 m.m. (110″) wide, fitted with turn-around for broadsiding, which rolls either plate or breakdowns for further hot rolling as in the Steckel hot mill described above. The breakdowns are rolled on five 66″ hot finishing stands in tandem and passed straight on to the runout table and coiler. Four finishing stands is the minimum. Cold rolling equipment is similar to that for the Steckel cold mill process described, except that two reversing mills are provided for tin plate. Fifty-six inch mills can also be used depending on the slab width.

4. *Semi-Continuous Hot Strip Mill and Tandem Cold Mills*

As with (3) above, the hot mill is semi-continuous employing a reversing roughing mill. The output is increased by rolling a larger slab at a higher frequency and to do this a further roughing stand is added and six finishing stands are provided. The extra roughing stand is usually non-reversing and follows the reversing rougher, to take an additional roughing pass on the breakdowns for the finishing mill. Plates are taken off between the reversing rougher and the non-reversing roughing stand.

Cold reduction is carried out on a four-stand tandem mill which rolls both sheet and tin plate gauges. To temper pass tin plate a two-stand temper mill is provided so that temper 3 and above may be rolled in one pass through the mill. One single-stand temper mill is provided for cold rolled sheet.

5. *Continuous Hot Strip Mill and Tandem Cold Mills*

For this process a fully continuous hot mill is proposed with four roughing stands and six finishing stands, none of which is reversing. To avoid cross rolling, plates above ⅜″ thick are not rolled as directional properties persist and output and yield are sacrificed if slabs are cross rolled. Plates up to this thickness are coiled on the hot coilers and subsequently uncoiled, leveled and cut up on the ⅜″ (9 m.m.) cut-up line.

Three continuous pickle lines are provided and the cold mills comprise one three-stand tandem mill for sheet, one five-stand tandem mill for tin plate and one four-stand tandem mill for light sheet and heavy tin plate gauges. Two two-stand tin plate temper mills are provided and three single-stand sheet temper mills.

A roughing scalebreaker (light two-high stand) is located immediately after the slab reheating furnaces in each process to crack the primary scale. A finishing scalebreaker (double pinch rolls with high pressure sprays) is located before the finishing stand in each process discussed previously.

One of the temper mills for cold rolled sheet in each process discussed above is a combined coil and sheet mill, to service small orders and wide sheets. Orders which do not make up a full coil weight are more economically cut up hard and annealed and tempered in sheet form. Good shape is more easily obtained on wider orders by the same method.

For each of the processes (2 through 5) electrolytic tin plate lines, or a combination of electrolytic and hot dipped tin plate can be added. The number of lines will depend upon the capacity in tin plate desired. For example, the continuous mill could easily turn out 600,000 tons of tin plate per year and would take four electrolytic lines. If the mechanized sheet mill was adopted, it would take hot dipped tinning facilities. For each of the processes described galvanizing facilities could be added.

6. *The I.C.C. Alternative 1*

This is essentially similar to the semi-continuous mill with reversing cold mills. It is a 56 inch hot mill, comprising a two-high (32 x 56 inch) scalebreaker, a four-high reversing rougher (32 inch and 54 x 56 inch), five four-high finishing stands, and one two-high skin pass mill (32 x 56 inch). Its cold mills consist of a Sendzimir Cold Reduction ZR21B-44 inch tin plate reversing mill, a cold reduction four-high reversing mill (21 inch and 54 x 56 inch), and a four-high temper rolling mill (18 inch and 53 x 56 inch).[3]

This mill will produce plates up to 48 inches wide and up to ½ inch thick; hot finished sheets and cold reduced sheets to 48 inches; and tin plate. Electrolytic tinning facilities and galvanizing facilities are also included.

7. *U. E. F. Alternative 1*

This is a semi-continuous layout with tandem cold mills. Its hot mill comprises one 110 inch 4 high reversing rougher, four 58 inch, 4 high finishing mills, one 56 inch 2 high skin pass mill. Its cold mills comprise one 56 inch 4 high 4 stand tandem cold mill, one 56 inch 4 high single stand temper mill. With relatively little expense the mills can be widened to handle 66 inch material for 60 inch finished products. An electrolytic tinning line and a galvanizing line is also part of their proposal. Provision is also made for plate finishing.

8. *U. E. F. Alternative 2*

To (7) previously discussed is added, in the hot mill, one 48 x 110 inch 2 high reversing rougher, and two 58 inch 4 high finishing mills. In the cold mill is added one 48 inch 4 high 5 stand tandem cold mill, and one 48 inch 4 high 2 stand tandem temper mill. Alternative 2 doubles the capacity of Alternative 1. Provision can be made in Alternative 2 for a separate plate rolling mill for 100 inch material, or for augmented plate finishing from the hot mills.

C. *Some Limitations of the Processes*

1. *The Mechanized Sheet and Tin Plate Mill*

The major limitations of the mechanized sheet and tin plate mill is, of course, the very limited capacity of this mill, and its in-

---

3. Provision is made for eventual conversion of the reversing 4 high cold mill into a 4 stand 4 high mill.

ability to produce plates and cold rolled sheets. It can produce tin plate, galvanized sheet stock, and other hot rolled sheets. Its unit costs are high, but its total investment is very low. It requires sheet bar as an input which would have to be imported.

2. *The Steckel Hot Strip Mill*

On a Steckel mill, due to the coiling process, the ends of the hot rolled strip are up to 0.014 inches thicker than the middle of the coil. This compares with "run down" variation of 0.005″ to 0.007″ in a continuous mill and 0.007″ to 0.010″ in a semi-continuous mill. As a consequence of this high "run down" the Steckel hot coil has irregular gauge. The use of one pair of rolls for five finishing passes in the Steckel process leads to bad surface and irregular shape in the hot coil. The Steckel also has flecked scale on the hot coil which arises from difficulty of descaling between cooling furnaces and mill. Some attempt has been made to reduce flecked scale by holding the breakdown and finishing at a lower temperature. But this results in inferior mechanical properties and the pickling process is made more difficult because there is more time for scale to form in the mill.

The gauge variations inseparable from the process mean that hot rolled coils from a Steckel mill cannot be rolled on a tandem cold mill. A reversing cold mill can, however, accept H. R. coil and reduce it successfully as the gauge variations can be made to match the normal variations of a reversing cold mill. The cost of this is in lower yield (see Tables 9 and 10). The surface condition means that no C. R. sheet better than General Purpose or drum stock can be made from a Steckel hot band, but C. R. tin plate can be successfully rolled again with some loss of yield.

For special steels and alloys such as stainless, silicon, titanium, etc., many of the above criticisms do not apply. In fact, where more than five or six passes in the finishing mill are required, a continuous or semi-continuous hot strip mill would be hopelessly uneconomic in view of the number of finishing stands needed so that a Steckel mill is the only solution for producing hot rolled coils of these alloy materials.

3. *Semi-Continuous Hot Strip Mill*

The only difference between this mill and the continuous hot strip mill is that the roughing train of four mills in the latter is replaced by a reversing rougher in the former This means that: (a) roughing time is longer, and (b) the same work rolls take all five roughing passes.

The result is that the run down is rather greater and the surface condition of the hot rolled strip slightly inferior. This last condition could be improved by changing rolls more often on the reversing rougher, but this would result in lower output rates and a consequent increase in operating costs.

The ultimate maximum tonnage of a semi-continuous mill is established by the time cycle at the rougher. This can, of course, be reduced (with improved run down) if a smaller slab is used. On the other hand the use of a smaller slab reduces coil size and tends to reduce yield at the cold mill (more welds and consequent off gauge).

4. *Continuous Hot Strip Mill*

The only limitation on a continuous mill is its inability to produce plate with transverse properties (no cross rolling) and the severe reduction in its output if plate thicker than 9 m.m. (which is usually the thickest that can be coiled with smooth operation) is produced. As a result, continuous mills usually do not roll plate thicker than 9 m.m. To remove the one-directional properties inherent in the process, the plates must be normalized. The installation of one wide roughing mill to make plate has not been found to be economically justified in this process.

5. *Reversing Cold Mills*

Although excellent for low outputs (sheet 30 t.p.h., tin plate 10 t.p.h.) reversing cold mills give low yields due to heavy tail ends; and gauge variations are greater than on tandem mills, due to the repeated acceleration and deceleration periods which occur every pass instead of once as on a tandem mill. This disadvantage will be reduced when automatic gauge control is installed.

To obtain the necessary reduction from H. R. coil to sheet (3 passes) and tin plate (5 passes) the interstand tension of a tandem mill has to be supplied by tension between the reversing mill and its coilers. The finished coil is therefore wound under a higher tension than one from a tandem mill. This does not matter in the case of tin plate which is rewound on the cleaning line. In the case of sheet, however, it results in a high proportion of stickers coming from annealing to the temper mill, which either means scrapping the coil or producing sheet after tempering with surface tears. This can be avoided by recoiling after cold reduction at a lower tension (extra cost) or taking a light finishing pass on the cold mill (reduced output). Surface finish and shape must also suffer where one pair of work rolls must, of necessity, be used for all passes of the cold reduction.

6. *Single Stand Temper Mills*

All tin plate above T_2 is normally tempered by giving it two passes through a single stand temper mill. Modern developments have led to the use of a two stand tandem temper mill so that all tempers can be produced in one pass. Single stand temper mills, therefore, have the disadvantage of low outputs on T_3 and above, and the extra coil damage inseparable from double handling of light gauge strip coils.

7. *Fly Shearing*

Hot finished sheets can be obtained either by fly shearing at the finishing train or coiling and subsequent shearing. For Extra Deep Drawing quality, flying sheared sheets must be cooled quickly and sheets cut cold from coil must be normalized. The flying shear limits the finishing speed and reduces output.

These limitations are of importance form an operational viewpoint. Though we do not ascribe a particular cost to each limitation, they can be of importance in selection of competing processes which are very close in total costs per ton of product.

D. *Investment Cost and Capacity of Flat Rolling Processes*

1. *Capacity*

The capacity of the flat rolling processes we have described cannot be compared exactly other than by comparison of the capacity of each item of equipment. Any actual plant will not be balanced in all its stages because of the discreteness of the capacity of each particular piece of equipment. For example, in the I. C. C. Alternative 1, the tin plate coil preparation line can handle 200,000 tons of coil at 7,200 hours operation, but the electrolytic tinning line can only produce 135,000 tons of tin plate at 7,200 hours operation. This latter figure is the maximum amount of tin plate that can be produced per year in the I. C. C. Alternative 1. Even when the most constraining bottlenecks are identified, the finished product capacity in each of the processes we describe (other than the mechanized sheet and tin plate mills) usually cannot be added since the products generally will use some common facilities, whose capacity will vary depending upon which product is being produced. Thus for example, the 4 Hi, Reversing Cold Mill of I. C. C. Alternative 1 can produce, at 7,200 hours of operation, 216,000 tons per year of cold reduced sheet coil, but since it must take 2 passes for cold reduced tin plate coil, it can only produce 108,000 tons of that product. Thus there is a trade off of capacity: one ton of tin plate coil uses as much capacity of this facility as 2 tons of sheet coil. It would clearly be erroneous to add 216,000 tons and 108,000 tons as the capacity of this particular piece of equipment. In general, the major bottlenecks are the capacity of the slabbing mill (in the case of Orinoco, the 1100 m.m. mill), the hot mills, and the basic cold mills. Other bottlenecks can exist, such as in tinning lines, cut up lines, annealing, temper mills, etc., but if space is available and provision made these units can be more easily added as demand warrants.

Bearing the above comments in mind, the single figure most often used to measure the capacity of the processes we are considering is the slab output (or in the case of the mechanized sheet and tin plate mills, the sheet bar output), which represents the slab requirements of some expected normal mix of finished products taken at the maximum capacity of these products at the most constraining bottleneck. In order to insure comparability we have measured this capacity at 6,000 hours of operation which is 3 shifts, 5 days per week, 50 weeks per year, 8 hours per shift. Though this is generally considered full capacity, it is of course possible to work 7,200 hours and occasionally even more for some equipment. Table 2 compares the slab output capacity of the processes.

TABLE 2

Capacity of Flat Rolling Processes at 6,000 Hours of Operation per Year. Metric Tons per Year.

Process	Thousands of Metric Tons Slab Output
Mechanized Sheet & Tin Plate Mill	74
Steckel & Reversing Cold Mill	350
Semi-Continuous & Reversing Cold Mill	500
I. C. C. Alternative 1	523[1]
Semi-Continuous & Tandem Cold Mills	800
U. E. F. "1970"	603
U. E. F. "1980"	1,180[2]
(Medium Size) Continuous and Tandem Cold Mills	2,500

[1]This is attainable in I. C. C. Alternative 1 only with approximately 7,000 hours operation of the one slab-reheating furnace specified in this alternative.

[2]Requires 7,150 hours of operation for the continuous annealing line and 8,000 hours for the single stack furnace annealing.

The finished flat products corresponding to these slab outputs, at a "normal" mix is shown in Table 3. As Table 3 shows, continuous hot mills with tandem cold mills are typically employed to produce cold rolled sheets and tin plate as their major product. They can of course produce far more light plates and hot rolled sheets than shown, if their plate and hot sheet finishing equipment (i.e., coilers, cut up lines, levellers, etc.) were designed for higher capacity. However, if this were done their capacity in tin plate and cold rolled sheets would be reduced for a given size hot mill. As high proportions of hot rolled finished products is an uneconomic use of a continuous mill (if the market exists for cold rolled products commensurate with the capacity of such an installation), these mills generally concentrate on the cold products.

TABLE 3

Finished Product Capacity of Flat Rolling Processes
At 6,000 Hours of Annual Operation

Process	Light Plates	Hot Rolled Sheets	Cold Rolled Sheets	Tin Plate
Mechanized Sheet Mill	—	40	—	20
Steckel & Reversing Cold Mills	40	39	95	68
Semi-Continuous & Reversing Cold Mills	80	55	144	98
I. C. C. Alternative 1	80	100	135	113
Semi-Continuous & Tandem	120	84	320	113
U. E. F. "1970" Proposal	65	150	200	100
U. E. F. "1980" Proposal	200	250	350	200
Continuous Hot Mill & Tandem Cold Mills	155	189	1,160	575

As both Tables 2 and 3 indicate the I. C. C. Alternative 1 and the U. E. F. "1970" and "1980" proposals are variants of the typical semi-continuous hot mill and reversing cold mill in the former case, and the semi-continuous and tandem cold mill in the latter case. The authors of the I. C. C. proposal recognize that if demand warrants, their proposal (Alternative 1) would at some later stage be converted into a tandem cold mill. The U. E. F. proposal "1970"—a particular staging of the "1980" proposal—is also a tandem cold mill operation. If the I. C. C. Alternative 1 was subsequently expanded it would become a semi-continuous hot mill and tandem cold mill layout. The U. E. F. proposals employ tandem cold mills from the beginning.

2. *Estimated Investment Cost of the Alternative Flat Rolling Proposals*

Exact investment costs are only obtained after firm bids have been received, and even these are somewhat modified during installation. But firm bids cannot be received unless prior analysis has determined the general specifications of the process, the initial capacities desired, and the ultimate capacities which can be achieved by modifications of the process. The purpose of this report is thus: to select the process or processes; the range of capacities both initial and ultimate for each of the flat products; and the staging and the phasing of this process which will yield an optimal expansion program when final judgment is made upon the values of the economic parameters (i.e., rate of interest, wage rates, depreciation period, and import penalty). Thus our present analysis may be viewed as the first stage of analysis—it sets the broad engineering-economic specifications of the expansion, and it gives a first approximation to the optimal staging and phasing of the expansion. When firm bids have been received, the final data (on investment costs, estimated operating costs, and the economic parameters mentioned above) can be reinserted into the model, and that staging and phasing of the process which yields a minimum cost can be finally determined. At our present stage of investigation, we can only use "fairly typical" investment and operating costs for "fairly typical" installations. But this data, we believe, is suitable for the purposes we have mentioned.

(a) *Sources of Data.* We have three sources of data, each referring to different time periods, and each differing in degree of detail. The most complete data referring to a similar time period and calculated on a uniform basis is the Cartwright-Dowding Report previously noted. This gives data on the five classical methods for fairly typical installations of these methods. This data is based upon 1955-1956 costs and is primarily founded on U. K. prices and experience. The I. C. C. proposals, made in the period April-July, 1963, are similarly based upon U. K. experience—though it is six years more recent. The United Engineering and Foundry tentative proposals drawn up at our request are, of course, based upon U. S. A. practice and is current as of January 1965. The U. E. F. cost of mechanical equipment (since they are steel mill equipment producers) may be taken as close figures to what an actual bid would reveal. As is usual in such cases, the figures are probably a little on the high side in order to protect the bidder when detailed bids are made against quoting a preliminary figure which subsequent calculations shows too low. Thus the figures of U. E. F. for mechanical equipment can be taken to be fairly close to a bid price. The U. E. F. estimates for electrical equipment may also be taken as fairly close approximations. The U. E. F. is one of the world's leading rolling mill producers and their electrical quotations are based upon close working relations with U. S. A. electrical equipment producers. We also have construction estimates made by U. E. F. But these estimates, in the view of officials of that Company, are only rough guesses based upon construction costs of similar facilities if they were installed in the U. S. A., based upon U. S. A. standards of heating, U. S. A. construction codes, U. S. A. amenities, etc. In order to make all of our estimates as comparable as possible, we have discarded the U. E. F. construction costs. Upon inspection of the site and soil, and with information on local construction labor costs, the U. E. F. will be able, if desired, to give more realistic construction estimates.

In general the most uncertain of the investment costs are those which relate to construction. However, the Cartwright-Dowding estimates have at least the virtue of being fairly complete and made upon a uniform basis—which we believe to be close to, though not exactly comparable with, the I. C. C. estimates of investment costs. We shall therefore present estimates of investment costs for the five classical methods based upon the Cartwright-Dowding estimates and updated to account for price increases from 1956-1965.[4] We shall also use the investment costs for the I. C. C. Alternative 1, and the U. E. F. 1970 and 1980 proposals, similarly updated and adjusted to make them comparable in terms of coverage, to the costs for the five classical methods.

(b) *Investment Cost Estimates.* Table 4 shows the percentage distribution of source of cost and total cost for each of the alternatives. Table 5 shows this in dollars at 1965 prices.

We have been unable to segregate for the I. C. C. estimate the investment values for services required by the mechanical and electrical equipment, or the miscellaneous category. However, we feel reasonably certain that these are included under the other I. C. C. categories. All the investment figures shown are without a figure usually included; i.e., a contingency allowance and an allowance for administration and engineering cost. Since these are usually proportional to the total investment and are simply a "fudge" factor, we have not included them at this stage of the anaylsis.

We should note that a serious discrepancy exists in the cost of transportation of the I. C. C. and all the other estimates. We have ascertained that this large discrepancy is not due to the differences in rough weight of the equipment in the various proposals, but to the price per ton of transportation assumed by the I. C. C. proposal. This computes out to $97.56 per ton for hot mill equipment and $88.95 per ton for cold mill equipment in the I. C. C. alternative. The Cartwright-Dowding transportation is given as $37 per ton for 1956. From what we have been able to ascertain, we believe the Cartwright-Dowding figures are much closer to the actual charge now, after being increased by 10%. If these transportation costs for I. C. C. were comparable to those

---

4. The inflationary price increase has been assumed to average 1 percent per year from 1956. Though cost of living data for Western Europe and Japan show far higher increases, export prices from these countries have generally risen less than the cost of living. Thus, for example, the International Monetary Fund shows the cost of living percentage increase since 1959 to the end of 1964 for the U. K., West Germany, Italy, France, U. S. A., and Japan to be 15, 13, 26, 23, 7, and 34 percent, respectively. It notes that the export price level for France and Western Germany has risen 10 percent since 1959. See *Wall Street Journal*, 1/27/65, p. 1.

TABLE 4

Percentage of Distribution by Source of Cost and Total Cost of Alternative Flat Rolling Processes

	(1) Mech. Sheet Mills	(2) Steckel & Revers. Cold Mills	(3) Semi-Cont. & Revers. Cold Mills	(4) Semi-Cont. & Tandem Cold Mills	(5) U.E.F. "1970"	(6) Adjusted I.C.C. Alt. 1	(7) U.E.F. "1980"	(8) Continuous & Tandem Cold Mills
Source				Process (Percent of Total Cost)				
1. Construction	38.1	36.0	35.9	36.6	29.9	29.0	36.6	31.1
2. Mechanical	39.0	31.2	31.8	32.2	35.7	30.6	30.4	34.6
3. Electrical	5.1	17.1	16.9	16.4	18.5	21.3	17.9	17.5
4. Cranes and Carriers	5.5	3.0	2.8	2.7	2.7	4.2	2.7	4.3
5. Operational Spares	4.7	5.3	5.5	5.3	6.3	6.3	5.7	5.7
6. Roll Maint. Shops	1.1	1.3	1.0	.9	.9	1.4	.9	.7
7. Build. and Mill Svs.	3.2	1.8	1.8	1.8	1.8	1.5	1.8	1.7
8. Svs., Mech. and Elect. Plant	.6	.8	.9	.8	.8	—	.8	.7
9. Transportation	.9	1.3	1.3	1.3	1.3	5.7	1.3	1.3
10. Miscellaneous	1.7	2.2	2.2	2.1	2.1	—	2.1	2.4
11. Total in 1956 dollars (000)	9,783	65,564	85,355	99,207	75,785[1]	79,282[2]	155,319[1]	211,086
12. Total in 1965 dollars (000)	10,761	72,120	93,891	109,128	75,785	80,868	155,319	232,195

SOURCE: Processes 1, 2, 3, 4 and 8—Cartwright and Dowding, *op. cit*, p. 23. I.C.C. Proposal "adjusted" Alt. 1, is based upon their submission to C.V.C. of Apr. 1963. The adjustment consists of updating their estimated cost of Alt. 1 (less allowances for contingencies, administration and engineering) by 1% per year 1963 to 1965, plus increasing their allowance for operational spares, so that it equals 10% of their mechanical cost plus 15% of their electrical cost. The U.E.F. proposals have been filled in by taking their mechanical and electrical costs (as of 12/15/64), adding the cost of operational spares (at 10% and 15% as above), and setting that total equal to the sum of the percentages shown for these items in Process 4. The figures of these three items were then converted to % of total. The 1970 cost of construction was estimated at 40% of the total (1970 and 1980) construction costs.

TABLE 5

Estimated Current (1965) Investment Cost by Source of Cost for Alternative Flat Rolling Processes

Source	(1) Mech. Sheet Mills	(2) Steckel & Revers. Cold Mills	(3) Semi-Cont. & Revers. Cold Mills	(4) Semi-Cont. & Tandem Cold Mills	(5) U.E.F. "1970"	(6) Adjusted I.C.C. Alt. 1	(7) U.E.F. "1980"	(8) Continuous & Tandem Cold Mills
				(Millions of Dollars)				
1. Construction	4.10	25.96	33.70	39.94	22.68	23.45	56.69	72.21
2. Mechanical	4.21	22.50	29.85	35.14	27.10	24.75	47.22	80.34
3. Electrical	.55	12.33	15.87	17.90	14.00	17.22	27.63	40.63
4. Cranes and Carriers	.59	2.16	2.63	2.95	2.05	3.40	4.19	9.98
5. Operational Spares	.51	3.82	5.16	5.78	4.81	5.09	8.85	13.24
6. Roll Maint. Shops	.12	.94	.94	.98	.68	1.13	1.40	1.63
7. Build. and Mill Svs.	.34	1.30	1.69	1.96	1.36	1.21	2.80	3.95
8. Svs., Mech. and Elect. Plant	.06	.58	.84	.87	.61	—	1.24	1.62
9. Transportation	.10	.94	1.22	1.42	.99	4.61	2.02	3.02
10. Miscellaneous	.18	1.59	2.06	2.29	1.59	—	3.26	5.57
11. Total[1]	10.77	72.12	93.89	109.13	75.79[2]	80.87[2]	155.32	232.20

[1]Will not exactly add to totals due to rounding
[2]See text for comment on these figures.

of the other processes shown, their total costs would be reduced by almost 3 million dollars or to about $77.7 million. Similarly, because of the mechanics of our adjustment procedure, we believe the estimate for the roll and bearing maintenance shops of the U. E. F. "1970" proposal is about $.40 million too low, and the transportation charges about $.35 million too low for the 1970 proposal. Thus the U. E. F. total investment figure for 1970 should be raised by about $.75 million to a total of about $76.5 million. This brings the U. E. F. 1970 and the adjusted I. C. C. Alternative 1 to within about $1.0 million of each other—which we believe, in view of the equipment involved in these proposals, should be approximately equal.

(c) *Capital Efficiency of the Alternate Processes.* The capital efficiency of the processes, defined as the capital outlay per ton of annual slab output of each of the processes, may be seen by comparing Table 2 and Table 5. This is shown in Table 6. Since the construction costs are, in our opinion, the least reliable in their application to Orinoco, we have shown the capital efficiency with and without estimated construction costs. The numbers after the "—" are the rank order of the processes in terms of efficiency.

It can be seen (particularly in the efficiencies based upon capital costs excluding construction) that the capital efficiency increases with the scale of the process, other than for the mechanized sheet and tin plate mills. This smallest of processes has a capital efficiency close to the semi-continuous hot mills with tandem cold mills. But as we note later, this process has very high operating costs and it cannot produce a full line of flats. One further point is worth noting—that is, that the semi-continuous mill with tandem cold mills represents a significant improvement over the semi-continuous setup with reversing cold mills in capital efficiency. But the gains in increasing scale of this process (semi-continuous with tandem cold mills) is very modest and reaches an asymptotic value near a slab output of about 1.250-1.500 million tons. Beyond this range, the capital efficiency can only

TABLE 6

Capital Efficiency of the Alternative Flat Rolling
Processes at 6,000 Hours of Annual Operation

Process	Annual Slab Output (000)	Total Investment Cost ($ millions)		Investment Cost per Slab Ton ($)	
		with const.	*excluding const.*	*with const.*	*excluding const.*
Mechanized Sheet Mills	74	10.77	6.67	146–6	90–6
Steckel & Revers. Cold Mills	350	72.12	46.16	206–8	132–8
Semi-Continuous & Reversing Cold Mills	500	93.89	60.19	188–7	120–7
I.C.C. Alt. 1, adjusted	523	77.70	54.25	149–5	104–5
Semi-Continuous and Tandem Cold Mills	800	109.13	69.19	136–4	86–3
U. E. F. "1970" Proposal	603	76.50	53.82	127–2	89–4
U. E. F. "1980" Proposal	1,180	155.32	98.63	132–3	84–2
Continuous and Tandem Cold Mills	2,500	232.20	159.99	93–1	64–1

be increased significantly in these processes by a jump to the fully continuous operation.

Table 7 shows a measure of the efficiency of the processes from a financial aspect. This measure is the potential annual revenue of the processes per dollar of investment. "Potential Revenue" is the revenue each process would generate operating at capacity. The prices used in this computation are U. S. A. prices as of October, 1964.

E. *Operating Costs of Flat Rolling Processes*

The major operating costs consist of the costs of metal input, labor input, productive services, and productive supplies. "Productive services" include power, heat, steam, and water required by the various processes. "Productive supplies" consist of a host of miscellaneous supplies including lubricating oils and greases, acid, tin, zinc, miscellaneous repair parts which are expended, oxygen, acetylene, paper, lumber, and so forth. These costs are "variable," that is to say, they are proportional to the output of each of the four basic flat rolled products. In addition to these

TABLE 7

Annual Revenue Potential of Alternative Flat Rolling Processes
At 6,000 Hours of Annual Operation

(Millions of Dollars)

Process	Total Revenue	Rev. Per Dollar of Investment	Plates	H.R. Sheets	C.R. Sheets	Tin Plate	Total Investment
Mechanized Sheet and Tin Plate	8.84	.821	—	4.75	—	4.09	10.77
Steckel and Revers. Cold Mills	37.51	.520	4.93	4.63	14.04	13.91	72.12
Semi-Cont. and Rev. Cold Mills	57.73	.615	9.87	6.53	21.28	20.05	93.89
I.C.C. Alternative 1	64.82	.834	9.87	11.88	19.95	23.12	77.70
Semi-Cont. and Tandem Cold Mills	95.20	.872	14.80	9.88	47.30	23.12	109.13
U.E.F. "1970" Proposal	75.86	.992	8.02	17.82	29.56	20.46	76.50
U.E.F. "1980" Proposal	147.00	.946	24.66	29.70	51.73	40.91	155.32
Cont. and Tandem Cold Mills	330.65	1.424	19.11	22.46	171.46	117.62	232.20

operating costs, there are "fixed costs" which we allocate to the various products. These costs consist of fixed charges arising from the investment required per ton of product capacity, and from the fixed labor costs; i.e., costs which correspond approximately to the "salaried labor" classification at Sidor. These fixed costs are treated in Section F.

1. *Physical Inputs and Factor Prices*

Because of the great variation in factor prices in different countries, the application of costs based upon foreign data to Venezuela are subject to serious error. This is particularly true of metal input, labor, power, heat, water and steam. Where possible, therefore, we have used physical inputs with prices of these inputs based upon our estimates of Venezuelan prices, applicable to Sidor. These prices are as follows.

TABLE 8

Prices of Major Inputs Used in the Analysis

Input	Unit	Price in B's
Slab	Metric Ton	309
Electric Power	KWH	.01
Heat	1 million Kg Calorie	2.160 (equivalent to .540 B's 10^6 BTU)
Steam	Kilograms	.002
Variable Labor	Man Hour	8.0 (includes Social Benefits)
Fixed Labor	Man Hour	10.0 (includes Social Benefits)
Scrap Credit	Metric Tons	151

It should be noted that the slab price is based upon the 1100 m.m. mill achieving the standard costs calculated in the report, "Operation of the Orinoco Steel Plant" (Table S 1). This slab cost does not include depreciation or interest on the investment associated with the 1100 m.m. mill. The figure of 309 B's per ton is lower by 21 B's per ton, than the cost used by the International Construction Company in their 1963 report. This difference in slab cost accounts for most of the difference in the costs we show for the I. C. C. Alternative 1 at full capacity, and the costs shown by the I. C. C. for their Alternative 1. The remaining difference between our costs and theirs, for their Alternative 1, is due to the fact that our operating costs are based upon full capacity in all products, whereas theirs is shown for a substantially smaller output. The costs of productive supplies which we use are based upon I. C. C. costs of productive supplies per ton of product, modified by the economies of scale shown by the various processes. To the extent that the 1100 m.m. mill does not achieve standard costs, all the costs which we have shown will be understated in absolute values. However, this factor will not change the relative standing of the alternate processes in terms of costs, though it could change the relative mix of local production versus imports.

2. *Metal Input Costs*

Metal input costs depend upon the yields which each process shows for each product, the cost of the input, and the credit for metal scrap generated. This is by far the largest single cost for all the flat rolled products, and underscores the importance of achieving efficiency in all the stages prior to flat rolling. Table 9 shows the yields for the various processes by products, and Table 10 shows the net metal input costs. The yields for the semi-contin-

TABLE 9

Yield of Finished Product from Slab and Ingot-Alternative Flat Rolling Processes

	Mechanized Sheet Mills		Steckel & Reversing Cold Mills		I.C.C. Semi-Cont. Hot Mills & Revers. Cold Mills		U.E.F. Semi-Cont. Hot Mills & Tandem Cold Mills		Continuous Hot Mills & Tandem Cold Mills	
					(%)					
Product	From Slab	From Ingot	From Slab	From Ingot	From Slab	From Ingot	From Slab	From Ingot	From Slab	From Ingot
Light and Medium Plates	—	—	80	68	80	68	89	76	89	76
Hot Rolled Sheets	82	70	78	66	88[2]	75	91	77	91	77
Cold Rolled Sheets[1]	—	—	67	57	84	71	84	71	86	73
Tin Plate	78	66	68	58	76	65	81	69	83	71

SOURCE: Mechanized Sheet Mills, Steckel & Reversing Cold Mills: W. F. Cartwright and M. F. Dowding, "Development of Flat Rolling in a Growing Economy." U.N. ST/ECLA/Con. 4/L.A. III-3. 1956.

I.C.C. and U.E.F.: From Proposals. Yields on continuous hot mills—U.S.A. industry sources. Yields are rounded to the nearest one percent.

[1]Refers to general purpose cold rolled sheets.
[2]Detailed calculation from I.C.C. shows 87.54%.

uous hot mill and the reversing cold mill processes are shown under the heading, "I. C. C."; the yields of the semi-continuous hot mill and tandem cold mills include the two U. E. F. proposals (i.e., U.E.F. "70" and "80") and are typical of classical process of this sort.

3. *Labor Input*

Table 11 shows the estimated variable man hours per ton of product and their cost of the eight alternative flat rolling proc-

TABLE 10

Net Metal Input Cost—Alternative Flat Rolling Processes

(B's per Ton)

Process	Plates	H.R. Sheets	C.R. Sheets	Tin Plate
Mechanized Sheet and Tin Plate Mills	—	530.0	—	550.2
Steckel and Reversing Cold Mills	352.3	357.9	394.3	390.4
I.C.C. Alternative 1 and Semi-Cont. and Reversing Cold Mills	352.3	332.6	342.0	363.7
U.E.F. "70" and "80" and Semi-Cont. and Tandem Cold Mills	330.4	326.2	342.0	349.6
Continuous and Tandem Cold Mills	330.4	326.2	337.2	344.5

NOTE: Slabs are costed at 309 B's per ton. See Table S-1, "Operation of the Orinoco Steel Plant," *op.cit.* Sheet Bars are costed at 459 B's per ton. Scrap is valued at 151 B's per ton. The slab cost is before depreciation and interest.

TABLE 11

Estimated Total Variable Man Hours and Cost per Ton of Flat Products—Alternative Flat Rolling Processes

(Hours and B's per Ton)

Process[1]	Light Plates (Hrs.)	Cost (B's)	H.R. Sheets (Hrs.)	Cost (B's)	C.R. Sheets (Hrs.)	Cost (B's)	Tin Plate (Hrs.)	Cost (B's)
1. Mechanized Sheet and Tin Plate Mills	—	—	14.6	116.8	—	—	31.6	252.8
2. Steckel and Revers. Cold Mills	4.2	33.6	3.3	26.4	4.6	36.8	8.2	65.6
3. Semi-Cont. and Rev. Cold Mills	2.9	23.2	2.0	16.0	2.9	23.2	5.6	44.8
4. I.C.C. Alt. 1	2.9	23.2	1.9	15.2	2.8	22.4	5.4	43.2
5. U.E.F "1970"	2.7	21.6	1.6	12.8	2.4	19.2	5.0	40.0
6. Semi-Cont. and Tandem Cold Mills	2.5	20.0	1.5	12.0	2.2	17.6	4.6	36.8
7. U.E.F. "1980"	2.4	19.2	1.4	11.2	2.0	16.0	4.3	34.4
8. Continuous and Tandem Cold Mills	1.0	8.0	1.2	9.6	1.6	12.8	3.6	28.8

Includes Production, Maintenance, Traffic, Inspection, Packing and all other functions in the process for which labor is not a fixed charge (i.e., salaried employees). Rate of 8 B's per hour for variable labor includes all social benefit costs.

[1]Note: In all tables subsequent to Table 11 in which processes are given by numbers, they refer to the process as numbered in Table 11 above.

esses. These include all variable man hours; i.e., production, maintenance, traffic, inspection, packing and so forth. It should be noted that the economies of scale with respect to man hours is marked—the continuous mill, for example, uses about 10 percent of the variable man hours per ton, compared to the smallest scale process. Even with respect to the medium scale processes, the continuous mill shows great man hour savings; a fact which has led advanced countries to employ these units with increasing frequency, since man hour prices in these countries are double and triple the rates prevailing in under-developed regions. The variable man hour input per ton of product output (as shown in Table 11) are those representative of Western European practice.[5] They are somewhat lower in the U. S. A., particularly for processes 5 through 8.

On the basis of the product capacity for the processes and the relationship between fixed and variable labor, the total number of employees has been estimated for fixed and variable between Production (including all functions other than maintenance) and Maintenance employees. It will be noted that the proportion of fixed employees to variable employees generally decreases with the scale of the process. Table 12 shows the estimated total employees at 750 shifts per year, by process segregated between fixed and variable for Production and Maintenance. Table 13 consolidated this information into total employees segregated between production and maintenance. The information in Table 12 provides a basis for determining the fixed labor expense to be allocated to each product by process. It is of some interest to note that total employees increase at a far lower rate as the output of a process approaches its capacity, than the output increase. This can be seen from the total employees we have estimated for I. C. C. Alternative 1 at capacity (857 employees),

---

5. The man hours shown for processes 4, 5 and 7 have been obtained by interpolation of the relationship shown (on a double log scale) between man hours and slab output, by product, for processes 1, 2, 3, 6 and 8 shown in the Cartwright-Dowding Study, *op. cit.*, to which has been added the hours required for electrolytic tin plate through the packing stage—based upon U. K. and U. S. A. experience for these stages.

TABLE 12

*Estimated Number of Fixed and Variable Employees Required
at 40 Hours per Week and 750 Shifts per Year to Produce
Capacity Output—Alternative Flat Rolling Processes*

Process	Total Fixed	Total Variable	Production Fixed	Production Variable	Maintenance Fixed	Maintenance Variable
Mechanized Sheet and Tin Plate Mills	102	613	92	558	10	55
Steckel and Reversing Cold Mills	137	643	88	497	49	146
Semi-Cont. and Revers. Cold Mills	148	653	88	473	60	180
I.C.C. Alt. 1	154	703	90	510	64	193
U.E.F. "1970"	145	702	85	525	60	177
Semi-Cont. and Tandem Cold Mills	156	818	91	610	65	208
U.E.F. "1980"	205	1,181	120	878	85	303
Continuous and Tandem Cold Mills	370	2,157	203	1,566	167	591

TABLE 13

*Estimated Total Number of Production and Maintenance
Employees Required at 40 Hours per Employee per Week to
Produce Capacity Output (750 Shifts per Year)—Alternative
Flat Rolling Processes*

Process	Total Employees	Production Employees	Maintenance Employees
Mechanized Sheet and Tin Plate Mills	715	650	65
Steckel and Reversing Cold Mills	780	585	195
Semi-Cont. and Reversing Cold Mills	801	561	240
I.C.C. Alternative 1	857	600	257
U.E.F. "1970"	847	610	237
Semi-Cont. and Tandem Cold Mills	974	701	273
U.E.F. "1980"	1,386	998	388
Continuous and Tandem Cold Mills	2,527	1,769	758

NOTE: For capacity output, see Table 3.

Employees include Fixed and Variable Employees, and includes all employees for production, maintenance, inspection, packing and shipping, in plant transportation of flat products, metallurgical and quality control of flat products, in plant record keeping of flat products. Does not include general works' employees which can be attributed to production, sales, and accounting of flat products. Variable employees have been increased by 10% for "relief" labor.

TABLE 14

Cost of Services and Production Supplies per Ton—Alternative Flat Rolling Processes

(B's per Ton)

Process	Plates	H.R. Sheets	C.R. Sheets	Tin Plate
Mechanized Sheet and Tin Plate Mill	—	57.5	—	158.2
Steckel and Reversing Cold Mills	32.7	38.9	79.5	163.0
Semi-Cont. and Reversing Cold Mills	29.0	32.2	66.4	153.1
I.C.C. Alternative 1	29.0	32.2	65.3	150.7
U.E.F. "1970"	29.0	32.2	61.4	147.5
Semi-Cont. and Tandem Cold Mills	29.0	32.2	56.1	138.9
U.E.F. "1980"	25.9	30.0	52.2	131.4
Continuous and Tandem Cold Mills	20.7	26.1	48.3	115.7

compared to 714 employees shown by the I. C. C. Corporation for their proposal operating at substantially below capacity.[6]

4. *Production Services and Supplies*

Table 14 shows the variable cost per ton of production services and production supplies, by each of the four flat products, for each of the eight processes. Though economies of scale are evident, these are not so marked as in man hour costs. It should be noted that these costs will be lower for Sidor (as the Orinoco Steel Plant is referred to) than for most foreign plants, because of the very low price of electric power and fuel (either fuel oil

---

6. That is, a slab consumption of 227,000 tons compared to about 525,000 tons.

or natural gas). For most foreign steel plants power cost will be between .8 cents and 1.1 cents per KWH, compared to .22 cents per KWH at Sidor. Similarly, heat will vary between 40 cents to 80 cents per million BTU's, compared to about 12 cents at Sidor. In producing tin plate, for example, a semi-continuous hot mill with reversing cold mills will consume about 490 KWH per ton (of which 90 KWH is for electrolytic tinning), while a continuous mill will consume about 355 KWH per ton. Thus Sidor does have substantial advantage because of its low power and heat prices.

5. *Recapitulation of Variable Operating Expenses per Ton*

Table 15 summarizes for each of the processes, by each of the products, the variable operating expenses per ton; comprising net metal input, labor, and production services and supplies.

F. *Fixed Costs by Process and Product*

1. *Fixed Labor Cost*

"Fixed" labor cost represents the cost of those employees whose number does not vary proportionately with the output of a particular product. For example, the superintendent of the cold mills will represent a "fixed" labor cost. However the labor we include as fixed does vary with the number of shifts. If the plant is working at 750 shifts per year (which we use as practical capacity), all the fixed employees shown in Table 16 are indeed "fixed." If, however, the plant works less than 750 shifts per year, some of these employees will not be used—i.e., they are not fixed. Thus our fixed labor cost is fixed with respect to the integral number of shifts. If 1.5 shifts are used per day, the fixed employees are the same as if 2.0 shifts are used per day. Similarly if 2.3 shifts are used, the fixed employees are the same as if 3 shifts were used. Thus the fixed costs represent a "burden cost" which decreases per unit of output as output increases, but whose total burden increases as the number of shifts increases from one per day to two per day to three per day.

TABLE 15

Estimated Variable Expense per Ton—Alternative
Flat Rolling Processes

	Process							
	1	2	3	4	5	6	7	8
				(B's per Ton)				
Plates								
Net Metal Input	—	352.3	352.3	330.4	330.4	330.4	330.4	330.4
Labor	—	33.6	23.2	23.2	21.6	20.0	19.2	8.0
Prod. Supp. & Srvs.	—	32.7	29.0	29.0	29.0	29.0	25.9	20.7
TOTAL		418.6	404.5	381.0	381.0	379.4	375.5	359.1
H. R. Sheets								
Net Metal Input	530.0	357.9	332.6	332.6	326.2	326.2	326.2	326.2
Labor	116.8	26.4	16.0	15.2	12.8	12.0	11.2	9.6
Prod. Supp. & Srvs.	57.5	38.9	32.2	32.2	32.2	32.2	30.0	26.1
TOTAL	704.3	423.2	380.8	380.0	371.2	370.4	367.4	361.9
C. R. Sheets								
Net Metal Input	—	394.3	342.0	342.0	342.0	342.0	342.0	337.2
Labor	—	36.8	23.2	22.4	19.2	17.6	16.0	12.8
Prod. Supp. & Srvs.	—	79.5	66.4	65.3	61.4	56.1	52.2	48.3
TOTAL		510.6	431.6	429.7	422.6	415.7	410.2	398.3
Tin Plate								
Net Metal Input	550.2	390.4	363.7	363.7	349.6	349.6	349.6	344.5
Labor	252.8	65.6	44.8	43.2	40.0	36.8	34.4	28.8
Prod. Supp. & Srvs.	158.2	163.0	153.1	150.7	147.5	138.9	131.4	115.7
TOTAL	961.2	619.0	561.6	557.6	537.1	525.3	515.4	489.0

NOTE: Based upon slab cost (excluding depreciation and interest) of 309 B's; Labor cost of 8 B's/HR including social benefits; Power costs of .01 B's/KWH; Heat cost of 2.16 B's/Million Kilogram Calories (.12 cents per million BTU); Steam costs of .002 B's/Kg. Productive Supplies include oils, greases, tin, acid, spelter roll use, miscellaneous repair parts; strapping, skids, paper, etc. Services include power, heat, steam and water.

We have determined the fixed labor expense, by product, by allocating the fixed number of employees shown in Table 16 (at 2000 man hours per employee) in proportion to slab tonnage consumed by each product at maximum product capacity. On the basis of U. S. A. practice, we have assumed that 35% of the fixed employees will be used on Shift 1; 35% on Shift 2; and 30% on Shift 3.

Table 16 shows the fixed man hours required per year for Shifts 1, 2, and 3 by product and by process. Table 17 converts this into Bolivars, on the assumption that the fixed man hours average 10 B's per man hour, counting social benefits.

TABLE 16

Allocation of Fixed Man Hours by Product by Shift

(*Thousands of Man Hours*)

Process	Plates Shift 1 & 2	Plates Shift 3	H.R. Sheets Shift 1 & 2	H.R. Sheets Shift 3	C.R. Sheets Shift 1 & 2	C.R. Sheets Shift 3	Tin Plate Shift 1 & 2	Tin Plate Shift 3
Mechanized Sheet & Tin Plate Mill	—	—	46.90	40.20	—	—	24.50	21.00
Steckel & Revers. Cold Mills	16.31	13.98	15.33	13.14	37.38	32.04	26.88	23.04
Semi-Cont. & Revers. Cold Mills	21.77	18.66	15.54	13.32	39.34	33.72	26.95	23.10
I.C.C. 1 (Alt.)	20.51	17.58	24.78	21.24	34.51	29.58	28.00	24.00
U.E.F. "1970"	13.23	11.34	29.47	25.26	39.55	33.90	19.25	16.50
Semi-Cont. & Tandem Cold Mills	20.72	17.76	14.21	12.18	54.60	46.80	19.67	16.86
U.E.F. "1980"	28.70	24.60	35.84	30.72	50.26	43.08	28.70	24.60
Continuous & Tandem Cold Mills	18.13	15.54	23.31	19.98	145.04	124.32	72.52	62.16

NOTE: Shifts 1 and 2 each take 35% of fixed man hours; Shift 3 takes 30%.

2. *Fixed Capital Cost*

The fixed capital costs depend on the total investment required by a process, and of course the depreciation period, the depreciation method, and the rate of interest that is desired for the capital invested. As we have noted, we use one depreciation period (15 years) and varying rates of interest. In conventional accounting capital costs are often times allocated to individual products, in order to arrive at individual product costs fully allocated and to guide pricing. In our analysis we do not allocate the capital costs, other than to the process. For once a process is chosen (or specified) the capital costs vary solely with the

TABLE 17

Fixed Labor Cost by Product, by Annual Output Range—Alternative Flat Rolling Processes

Process — Output Range (000 Tons) / Cost (000 B's)

Product	(1) Output Range	(1) Cost	(2) Output Range	(2) Cost	(3) Output Range	(3) Cost	(4) Output Range	(4) Cost	(5) Output Range	(5) Cost	(6) Output Range	(6) Cost	(7) Output Range	(7) Cost	(8) Output Range	(8) Cost
Plates	0 -14	—	1-14	163	1-28	218	1-28	205	1-23	132	1-42	207	1-70	287	1-54	181
	14 -28	—	14-28	326	28-56	436	28-56	410	23-46	264	42-84	414	70-140	574	54-108	262
	28 -40	—	28-40	466	56-80	623	56-80	586	46-65	377	84-120	592	140-200	820	108-155	417
H.R. Sheets	0 -14	470	1-14	153	1-19	155	1-35	248	1-52	295	1-29	142	1-87	358	1-66	233
	14 -28	940	14-28	306	19-38	310	35-70	496	52-104	590	29-58	284	87-174	716	66-132	466
	28 -40	1342	28-39	437	38-55	443	70-100	708	104-150	843	58-84	406	174-250	1023	132-189	666
C.R. Sheets	—	—	1-33	374	1-50	393	1-47	345	1-70	396	1-112	546	1-122	503	1-406	1450
	—	—	33-66	748	50-100	786	47-94	690	70-140	792	112-224	1092	122-244	1006	406-812	2900
	—	—	66-90	1068	101-144	1123	94-135	986	140-200	1131	224-320	1560	244-350	1437	812-1160	4143
Tin Plates	0 - 7.0	245	1-24	269	1-34	270	1-34	280	1-35	193	1-39	197	1-70	287	1-201	725
	7.1-14.0	490	24-48	538	34-68	540	39-78	560	35-70	386	39-78	394	70-140	574	201-402	1450
	14.1-20.0	700	48-68	768	68-98	771	78-113	800	70-100	551	78-113	563	140-200	820	402-575	2072

SOURCE: Tables 29 and 42.

process (and its capacity). Thus process 4 (I. C. C. Alt. 1) has a capability of producing each of the four flat products and in considering this process as a contender, against all the other processes which can produce the four products, we need to know only the absolute size of the fixed investment cost of each process and its capacity. We therefore simplify our computations at this stage by not allocating investment cost to products.

G. *Advantages and Limitations of Staging*

The primary purpose of staging is to conserve capital without giving up the advantages of more efficient and larger capacity processes. Staging also has a collateral advantage of reducing training expenses, since operational mistakes are limited to the particular stage installed.

In integrated staging the conservation of capital results from installing less than the full capacity of the process. In the U. E. F. 1980 proposal, for example, at least 1 million tons of plates, sheets, and tin plate can be produced in total. If this process were installed completely, say by 1970, there would be a large amount of excess capacity—at least through some period of the decade 1970-1980, if our requirements are near the mark. To avoid this waste of capital (excess capacity) the process is scaled down. This scaling down is an integrated scaling down of capacity, which in the U. E. F. case is their 1970 proposal. The advantage then is that the installed capacity of integrated staging is always closer to estimated requirements at any time during the planning period than if the maximum capacity of the process was installed completely at some particular time during the planning period. Thus capital is conserved.

It is important to note that all staging requires the following:

(a) Knowledge of the complete plan; i.e., the investment and operating costs of the process at its maximum capability.

(b) The investment, capacity, and operating costs of each of the stages.

(c) Provision in construction, design, and installation for efficient adding of stages.

(d) Correct determination as to when the stages should be installed; i.e., when the capacity should be operational.

A correct solution of the staging and phasing problem is, of course, the core of the solution of the steel expansion problem (or any industrial expansion problem) in a country which expects or is planning for long sustained growth. As we have shown, this problem cannot be solved simply or intuitively.

Non-integrated staging uses less capital at the time of staging than integrated staging. Thus if one installs an electrolytic tinning line, rather than a semi-continuous hot sheet mill and cold reduction mills, much less capital is required. But this advantage is obtained usually at the price of higher operating costs since material purchased from the outside is more expensive than if the inputs were made by the process. However, some degree of non-integrated staging may be an optimal staging method depending upon the magnitudes of the rate of interest, the operating costs, and the errors in the estimated requirements of other products (produced by the integrated process). If the cost of capital is very high, the error in the estimates of other products are large as compared to the product produced by the non-integrated stage; the social cost of imports are very low and the difference in operating costs are low; then some degree of non-integrated staging may prove optimal. In the case of the Estudio proposal for an electrolytic tinning line, one might argue that tin plate requirements have less error in the short period (say the next five years) than hot sheets, cold sheets, and plates. Hence, install the electrolytic line and wait until more information on the requirements of the other products is obtained. Of course, the wisdom of this plan can only be tested by comparing it with the alternative methods of staging; i.e., with the total costs per unit of product produced (and imported). Though it is true that tin plate requirements in the short period can be estimated more accurately than the requirements of the other flat products, and though it might be sold at some profit (if the price of tin plate is increased), these facts alone do not demonstrate the soundness of the plan.

The limitations of staging are as follows:

(a) Construction costs are usually more expensive due to the fixed costs involved in assembling crews, equipment, and design teams at each installation.

(b) Some interruption of operation is inevitable at each installation.

(e) The inflationary factor makes both equipment and construction, and engineering more expensive when a process is built in stages, than when it is installed completly from the beginning. Offsetting this factor may be improvements in equipment and construction technique, so that later installations may be more efficient than earlier ones.

(d) In addition to these disadvantages, non-integrated staging has the further disadvantage of having to import semi-finished materials, and of maintaining larger stocks of these materials (than if they were locally produced), both in plant and in transit. In addition there are also the warehousing and multiple handling costs associated with these stocks.

3.   *Estimates of Additional Costs Due to Staging*

There are additional costs involved in both integrated and non-integrated staging, which must be estimated in order to properly evaluate whether staging is part of an optimal strategy of expansion.

(a) *Construction.* For the reasons previously mentioned, construction costs of a staged process are higher than those of an unstaged process. These costs vary greatly, depending upon the amount of construction initially done in anticipation that at some future date additional equipment will be installed. General steel mill construction practice, when expansion is staged, is to drive all piling needed, and provide all foundations for equipment which is close together but not installed at the same time. This practice minimizes interruption to production when adding equipment.

We are assuming this practice in all our estimates of staging. Nevertheless, there are unavoidable increases in construction costs in staging, particularly in remote areas such as Mantanzas. Heavy equipment must be assembled several times rather than once; construction crews must be recruited several times; temporary structures, road access, etc. must be provided and torn down several times; engineering prints and planning must be kept up-to-date; and revisions (due to unforeseen changes during the stages) must be made. We have been advised that the increase in construction costs due to staging average about 7.5 percent. This estimate does not assume price increases in construction labor, equipment, services, or engineering. Both integrated and non-integrated staging are subject to these additional costs. Table 18 shows the estimated construction costs for hot mills and cold mills, staged and unstaged.

(b) *Interruption Expense.* The major effects of staging on operating costs are different for integrated and non-integrated staging. Both types are subject to production interruptions when equipment is added. These delay costs can be substantial—particularly if provision is not made initially for foundations and piling for future equipment. However, as we have noted, staging does have some production efficiencies compared to unstaged expansion. Training costs are less, and defective production costs are limited. We believe that interruption costs when construction is properly planned in a staged process, will be nearly offset by training economies of a staged expansion. We have not, therefore, included a penalty for interruption costs.

(c) *Expenses of Additional Inventory.* Non-integrated staging is subject to expenses of additional inventory, as a result of the necessity of importing semi-finished raw materials. For example, if a tinning facility were built, and no other equipment were built, the tinning facility would operate upon imported cold reduced black plate coils. Similarly if cold mills were installed, but not hot mills, the cold mills would have to operate upon imported hot rolled coils. These semi-finished materials would have

TABLE 18

Increase in Investment Cost Due to Construction Increase Resulting from Staging Expansion—Alternative Flat Rolling Processes

($ Millions)

Process	Total Investment Not Staged	Additional Const. Costs of Staging	Staged Total Investment	Staged Investment Costs of	
				Cold Mills	Hot Mills
1. Mechanized Sheet & Tin Plate Mills	10.77	—	10.77	—	—
2. Steckel & Reversing Cold Mills	72.12	1.95	74.07	40.00	34.07
3. Semi-Cont. & Reversing Cold Mills	93.89	2.53	96.42	52.07	44.35
4. I.C.C. Alternative 1	77.70	1.76	79.46	42.91	36.55
5. U.E.F. "1970"	76.50	1.70	78.20	42.23	35.97
6. Semi-Cont. & Tandem Cold Mills	109.13	3.00	112.13	60.55	51.58
7. U.E.F. "1980"	155.32	4.25	159.57	86.17	73.40
8. Continuous & Tandem Cold Mills	232.20	5.42	237.62	128.31	109.31

SOURCE: Construction Cost Not Staged—Table 5. Construction Costs Staged = 1.075 × Construction Cost Not Staged. Cold Mills equals 54% of total investment; Hot Mills = 44% of total investment.

to be imported from overseas; i.e., either Japan, Western Europe or North America. There are also many other hidden costs of non-integrated staging which must be taken into consideration. We have made estimates of these as well, which are included in the costs of the appropriate processes in these various degrees of staging.

PUBLICATIONS OF THE DIVISION OF RESEARCH

AGRICULTURAL MARKET ANALYSIS
Vernon L. Sorenson, editor

LABOR MARKET INSTITUTIONS AND WAGES IN THE
LODGING INDUSTRY
John P. Henderson

THE EXECUTIVE IN CRISIS
Eugene Emerson Jennings

BANKING STRUCTURE IN MICHIGAN: 1945-1963
Robert F. Lanzillotti

RETAIL DECENTRALIZATION
Eli P. Cox and Leo G. Erickson

BANK ADMINISTERED POOLED EQUITY FUNDS FOR
EMPLOYEE BENEFIT PLANS
Frank L. Voorheis

THE PERFORMANCE POST AUDIT IN STATE GOVERNMENT
Lennis M. Knighton

PASSENGER TRANSPORTATION
Stanley C. Hollander

A SELECTED AND ANNOTATED BIBLIOGRAPHY ON
SHOPPING CENTER MANAGEMENT
Bernard J. La Londe and Paul E. Smith

INSTITUTE FOR INTERNATIONAL BUSINESS AND ECONOMIC
DEVELOPMENT STUDIES

MSU International Business and Economic Studies

MICHIGAN'S COMMERCE AND COMMERCIAL POLICY STUDY
John L. Hazard

INTERNATIONAL DIMENSIONS IN BUSINESS
Recent Readings from BUSINESS TOPICS

MANAGEMENT DEVELOPMENT AND EDUCATION IN THE SOVIET UNION
Barry M. Richman